UNDERSTANDING NHS DENTIST
PREPARING FOR THE FUTURE

ABOUT THE AUTHORS

Len D'Cruz BDS LDS LLM MFGDP DipFOd PGC Med Ed

Len D'Cruz qualified from the Royal London Hospital in 1989 and did his vocational training at Whipps Cross. He runs a five-surgery practice in Woodford Green with his wife Anne who is also a dentist. He has been a vocational trainer for a number of years and his practice is both Denplan accredited and also a BDA Good Practice Scheme Silver member. He is an MJDF Examiner for the FGDP(UK). He currently splits his time between clinical general dental practice, work as a dento-legal adviser for Dental Protection Ltd and as Dental Practice Adviser for two London-based PCTs. He is also a Dental Postgraduate Tutor for the Eastern Deanery. He has written *Legal Aspects of General Dental Practice* (Elsevier/Churchill Livingstone) and has had many articles published in the dental press. He was series editor and contributor of the BDJ series *Risk Management in General Practice*. He is on the Editorial Board of the journal *Private Dentistry*. He lectures widely on the NHS and medico-legal aspects of dental practice.

Raj Rattan MBE BDS MFGDP FFGDP Dip.MDE

Raj Rattan is a general dental practitioner and Associate Dean in the London Deanery. He is a dento-legal adviser at Dental Protection Ltd. He is a member of the FGDP(UK), a former examiner for MFGDP and was the consulting editor of the Key Skills CD programme. He has a long-standing interest in publishing as a writer, publisher and editorial content adviser. He has published numerous articles in the dental press, has authored/co-authored seven textbooks on various aspects of dentistry and has been closely involved with a number of e-learning initiatives and in the development of a number of interactive CD-ROM-based training packages. A former Government Policy Adviser, Raj continues to act as a consultant/professional adviser to a number of NHS and private sector organisations. He has lectured extensively both in the UK and overseas on many aspects of general dental practice and he been voted amongst the Top Ten most influential dentists in the UK on numerous occasions. He was appointed MBE in the 2008 New Year Honours List for services to the dental profession.

Michael Watson OBE BDS BSC(Econ)

Michael Watson practised dentistry as an army officer then in general dental practice until 1991. He then joined the staff of the British Dental Association (BDA); while there he held a number of posts including editor of *BDA News* and Special Adviser. The latter role encompassed the remuneration and contracts of GDPs and involved working with politicians and officials from the Department of Health. Since retiring from the BDA he has written extensively in the dental press, contributing both information and opinion pieces. He has also provided consultancy and advisory services on the new dental contract. He contributed a session on dental contracts across the UK to the electronic learning project e-den, sponsored jointly by the UK dental faculties and the Department of Health. He is still closely involved with the activities of the British Dental Association. In 2002 he was appointed OBE for services to the dental profession.

LEN D'CRUZ   RAJ RATTAN   MICHAEL WATSON

Understanding NHS Dentistry

PREPARING FOR THE FUTURE

DENTAL PUBLISHING

LONDON 2010

This edition of *Understanding NHS Dentistry –
Preparing for the Future* first published in 2010 by
Dental Publishing Limited, PO Box 66763, London WC1A 9EW

First published as *Understanding NHS Dentistry* in 2006 by
New Contract Help Publications

A catalogue record for this book is available from the British Library.

Cover image from Stock.XCHNG (www.sxc.hu)

ISBN: 978-0-9566723-0-8

Printed by Butler, Tanner and Dennis, Frome

Contents

HOW TO USE THIS BOOK

This is a book for all members of the dental team. Following on from the first, highly successful edition of *Understanding NHS Dentistry* – which appeared shortly after the introduction of the new dental contract in 2006 – this second edition has been completely rewritten to take account of the practicalities of working within the new system, and will help prepare the dental team for the changes promised by the new Government.

The long-term success of practices will depend on their grasp of the big picture and their understanding of how commissioning works. With a new vocabulary to acquire and unfamiliar concepts to embrace, dentists have a steep learning curve to master the new system's processes and relationships: this book will help you do that.

Divided into four sections, *Understanding NHS Dentistry* explains:

- how the system works now and the ways in which commissioning may change in the future
- how to work with the contract, including patient care and services you provide
- running a practice, including finance, contract monitoring, disputes and complaints
- business considerations and how you can manage change.

There are three ways to use this book:

- As a reference book, when you need a certain point clarified
- As an educational resource to learn about issues such as commissioning, clinical governance and business considerations
- As a pointer to the future, helping you to understand changes that are likely to happen in the coming years.

▶ pp 95–208.

▶ pp 209–231.

▶ pp 1–46.

▶ pp 47–94.

Practice owners and those who hold contracts with PCTs will be particularly interested in Part Three, 'Running a practice' and Part Four, 'Future planning'. **Associates and Performers**, especially those new to the NHS, will concentrate more on Part One, 'Introduction to the contract' and Part Two, 'Working with the contract'. *All* members of the dental team will find the book illuminating and educational.

Part 1 – Introduction to the contract

Part One starts with a brief overview of the 2006 contract, covering who's who, the types of contract, regulations and services as well as where you can get more information. 'Setting the scene' takes the reader through the various attempts to reform the dental contract, going back to 1964 and coming forward to the 2010 White Paper; as such, this chapter points the way to future developments. Commissioning both now and in the future is covered in the next chapter. The final chapter, 'The dental team working together', will be especially useful for those new to the NHS, showing where they fit within both the practice and the profession.

Part 2 – Working with the contract

This part answers the questions that arise in the day-to-day running of a practice: taking on patients, the services you offer, as well as the complications that can arise when trying to deliver good patient care. It addresses questions such as:

- What are UDAs?
- What is in each patient charge band?
- What is meant by 'all necessary care and treatment'?
- How often should I recall patients?
- When can I 'mix' private and NHS treatment?
- When and how should I refer patients?

Part 3 – Running a practice

As its title suggests, this part is aimed primarily at practice owners and Contractors, but associates and Performers need to know how a practice works and why they are being asked to work in a particular way. It examines good working relationships between owners and associates, how your contract value is made up and divided between dentists in the practice. It also deals with some of the less welcome sides of the contract: monitoring, disputes and complaints. Finally, there is a chapter on understanding clinical governance and what is needed for compliance.

Part 4 – Future planning

The changes which have come about since 2006 'necessitate a radical rethink of the business model of running a general dental practice and require dentists to revisit their business strategy.' This is the focus of the fourth and final part of the book. The next few years will be characterised by continuing change; managing this will be the challenge for practices in the future.

Wales

The book is also relevant to readers in Wales, despite some differences in NHS dentistry there. The regulations are the responsibility of the Welsh Assembly Government but, for the most part, mirror those in England. Most of the differences relate to the different structure there. The most obvious of these is that there are no Primary Care Trusts in Wales, the equivalent organisation there being Local Health Boards. There are seven of these in the country, following a reorganisation in 2009. Details of the reorganised structure of NHS Wales can be found on the *Health in Wales* website.

Details of structure of NHS Wales can be found at: www.wales.nhs.uk/ nhswalesaboutus/structure

Dental patient charges in Wales have been frozen at the 2006 level since then. In Wales, dental examinations are free to people aged under 25 or aged 60. There are also no prescription charges there. Apart from these differences other aspects of the charging regime are the same in England and Wales.

wales.gov.uk/topics/health/ocmo/ professionals/dental/?lang=en

♦ pp x–xii.

In 2007 a Task and Finish Group reported to the Welsh Health Minister on issues surrounding the introduction of the new contract in 2006. Meetings on its findings continue and readers who want more information should look on the website of the Chief Dental Officer for Wales. Discussions are ongoing between the English and Welsh Governments on the changes proposed in the Department of Health's 2010 White Paper.

Preface: PREPARING FOR THE FUTURE

The NHS White Paper

In July 2010, the Coalition government published a White Paper – *Equity and excellence: Liberating the NHS*. This concerned the future of the NHS in England only and will require a new Health Act to bring its provisions into force. For NHS dentistry a new contract is promised:

> Following consultation and piloting, we will introduce a new dentistry contract, with a focus on improving quality, achieving good dental health and increasing access to NHS dentistry, and an additional focus on the oral health of schoolchildren.

Para 3.22 page 26

The other major change to affect NHS dentistry is that Primary Care Trusts (PCTs) are to be abolished; their secondary care commissioning functions – mainly concerned with hospital services – will be taken over by general practitioner consortia. Local commissioning of primary care dental services through PCTs will continue until 2013. Afterwards, commissioning will be the responsibility of a new NHS Commissioning Board, to be set up in April 2012. This will have the responsibility of allocating budgets to, and supervising the commissioning role of, GP consortia. These changes are subject to a public consultation.

The Board will also be directly responsible for commissioning services that GPs themselves provide as well as the other family health services of dentistry, community pharmacy and primary ophthalmic services.

There will be a new Public Health Service, with a ring-fenced budget. PCT responsibilities for local health improvement will transfer to local authorities, who will employ the Director of Public Health jointly appointed with the Public Health Service. Local Directors of Public Health will be responsible for health improvement funds allocated according to relative population health need.

The consultation and piloting of a new NHS dental contract will take some time. In the meanwhile, practices will be operating under the contracts they hold with their local PCT. It seems likely that the new contract will

Figure 1: *Equity and excellence: Liberating the NHS*, Department of Health July 2010, CM7881. www.dh.gov.uk/en/Healthcare/ LiberatingtheNHS/index.htm

be a nationally applied one and that dentists will be in contract with the new NHS Commissioning Board by April 2013.

Working with the existing contract

However, during the next three years dentists will be operating within their existing contracts. This means working with PCTs, even though they will be running down in the period up to their abolition in 2013.

® NHS (General Dental Services Contracts) 2006 (GR 5123) and ® NHS (Personal Dental Services Agreements) 2006 (GR 5124). ® NHS (Dental Charges) 2006, ® NHS (Performers Lists) Amendment 2005; GDS and PDS Statement of Financial Entitlements. DH, updated annually (GR 5992).

In 2006 there was a standard General Dental Services (GDS) contract and a standard Personal Dental Services (PDS) Agreement. These were based on GDS and PDS Regulations and various other regulations that came in at the same time. Funding for NHS dentistry was also ring-fenced and payments to dentists were governed by directions laid down by the Secretary of State for Health. These regulations still govern contracts throughout England and Wales and will do so until new regulations are framed.

What has changed, and what makes this book essential reading, is that PCTs have been able to interpret and vary contracts, largely with the consent of dentists but within the overall regulatory framework. Appeals on various points of contracts – heard by the NHS Litigation Authority – have begun to establish some 'case law'. The authors have revised the text in the light of these different interpretations.

⬧ Chapter 13, 'Disputes, sanctions and appeals', p 158.

⬧ Chapter 5, 'Contracting models', p 54.
⬧ Chapter 2, 'Setting the scene', p 15.

In 2009 the Dental Access Programme launched a new and complex contract for volunteer practices: the PDS Plus Agreement. In addition, April 2010 saw an initial wave of pioneer pilots starting to test the recommendations of the 2009 Steele Review. Despite the changes over the last years, the framework within which dentists' contracts operate remains substantially the same as it was in 2006. The NHS contract is one that allows for local commissioning through PCTs and will remain so for the few years, although economic circumstances may dictate that fewer new practices are established.

Preparing for the future

While working under the existing system practices should now be preparing for a new contract which, as already stated, will have a focus on:

- improving quality
- achieving good dental health
- increasing access to NHS dentistry
- the oral health of schoolchildren.

In the White Paper the Government says it will have policy of 'putting patients first': *No decision about me without me* is their slogan. The White Paper says:

> First, patients will be at the heart of everything we do. So they will have more choice and control, helped by easy access to the informa-

'Foreword', p 1.

tion they need about the best GPs and hospitals. Patients will be in charge of making decisions about their care.

In the new NHS, patients will have more choice; this principle is likely to extend into dentistry. This means shared decision-making about their treatment and access to the information they need to make choices about their care. They will be able to rate hospitals according to the quality of care they receive, and this could well extend into primary dental care. Finally, the Government says it will strengthen the collective voice of patients and the public. One of the aims of this book is to help dentists and their teams prepare for a future where the patient's voice is louder, in both decision-making and in public.

Improving healthcare outcomes and implementing quality standards are two other themes of the White Paper. According to this,

¶3.2, p 1.

> The primary purpose of the NHS is to improve the outcomes of healthcare for all: to deliver care that is safer, more effective, and that provides a better experience for patients.

In the new NHS there will be less emphasis on targets and more on outcomes. The proposed NHS Commissioning Board, set to commission NHS dentistry after 2013, will operate according to these principles. This book aims to help you meet the current targets, while preparing for an NHS based on outcomes.

Work is proceeding on changes to the existing contract and the piloting of what may in the end become the new contract. The dentistry Minister has spoken of this as based on registration, capitation and quality: details are scheduled to be published in December 2010. These aspects are explained in the book to enable practices to develop flexibility when 'preparing for the future'.

Care Quality Commission

See CQC website:
www.cqc.org.uk/
Go to Guidance for professionals –
primary dental care.

From 1 April 2011, all dental practices in England, whether NHS, private or mixed must be registered with the Care Quality Commission (CQC). Its website gives guidance on how to register, who has to register and about the standards of quality and safety required. Letters were sent out by the CQC to dentists in September 2010 inviting them to take part in the registration process.

Dentists can register as individuals, partners or organisations; you need to study the guidance to see which applies to you. The website also contains guidance on compliance with essential standards of quality and safety. Applications will be made from November 2010 and registration must be complete by the end of March 2011.

FOREWORD

Four years ago, when I happily accepted the authors' invitation to write the Foreword to their original book that this new edition has now superseded, I never imagined for a moment that so much change could possibly overtake such a substantially reformed new system so radically, and so quickly. I did say at the time that the new (2006) system would be evolving before the ink of that original book was dry – and I was certainly proved right – but nothing is more certain than the fact that the same fate will befall this latest edition.

There was a case to be argued for waiting until there was greater clarity about where NHS dentistry in England and Wales will finish up, but this would have denied many people the opportunity to bring themselves up to speed with where we are now – and more importantly, to start preparing themselves and their practices for the future. Whatever happens, there will be a further three years before any further major legislative changes will come into force, and in the meanwhile, services will still need to be commissioned and patients will still need to be treated. Having incorrect and outdated information 'out there' in an authoritative practical reference source such as this is an ever present risk faced by every author of this kind of material, but the greater risk is carried by those who might act upon the information without realising that the world has moved on.

We already know a lot more now than we did in 2006 about how the new dental contract works in practice, and where the pitfalls are for the unwary. This in itself is more than sufficient justification for the decision to update the text and publish this second edition.

Just as with the first edition, anyone who is involved in NHS primary care dentistry in England and Wales – whether commissioning it, contracting to provide it, or actually delivering it – stands to benefit from spending time with this book. I choose these words carefully, because this is a book to refer to, to think about and reflect upon, to go back to and read again in a different context, or in the light of fresh experience. It is not a 'page turner' that one simply reads from flysheet to back cover and then discards.

Every member of the practice team has a stake in the future shape of NHS dentistry. That future may or may not be as committed to the delivery of NHS dentistry, as had been the case with so many practices under the pre-2006 fee-per-item remuneration system, and for this reason the authors have chosen wisely in targeting the areas for the greatest revision from the original text. The sections on commissioning, monitoring your contract and quality and clinical governance have emerged particularly well from the process.

◗ Chapters 3 (pp 21–38), 11 (pp 126–33) and 16 (pp 210–18).

No matter how great or diminutive your NHS commitment, no matter how much or how little experience of the 2006 contract you have, this book walks every reader through the mysteries, the jargon and the practicalities of NHS dentistry at a time of massive upheaval and transition for practices, practice owners, dental health professionals and, not least, patients.

Kevin Lewis BDS FDS RCS FFGDP
Dental Director, Dental Protection Limited

Part One

INTRODUCTION TO
THE CONTRACT

1 THE 2006 CONTRACT – AN OVERVIEW

Local Health Boards in Wales: ◗ 'How to use this book', p ix.

In the run up to April 2006 dentists in the NHS were offered a standard contract by their Primary Care Trust (PCT). On a local level PCTs have always had the ability to modify the standard contract to suit their circumstances. Many did this for new contracts issued and some have been seeking to agree variations to existing contracts.

This book describes the framework within which contracts must be written. It may well be that if you apply for a new contract you will be asked to sign something very different from what you have had before, or you may be asked to agree a variation to your existing contract. In making changes, however, the PCT must ensure that the new contract is written in accordance with the regulations and, if it is a variation to an existing contract, you must agree the changes.

Who's who

Unfamiliar terms entered the dental dictionary with the coming of the 2006 contract.

◗ Chapter 3, 'Commissioning', p 20.

◗ Chapter 4, 'The dental team working together', p 40.

- **Commissioner** – usually the PCT.
- **Contractor** (aka **Contract Holder**, **Provider** or **Practice Owner**) – a dentist, partnership or corporate body.
- **Performer** – a dentist who sees the patients, whether a practice owner (a 'Provider/Performer') or an associate.

A major difference between the old and new arrangements was that pre-2006 almost all dentists had an individual contract with the NHS, whereas now it is mainly practice owners.

Contractors

Contractors are normally the practice owners. They are often, but do not have to be, Performers and have responsibility for the whole contract. This includes receiving money from the PCT and patients and distributing it to associates and staff, as well as paying the bills. They are also responsible for delivery of the contract and will be monitored by PCTs on this. They

♦ Chapter 16, 'Quality and clinical governance', p 183.

must set up protocols for complaints and clinical governance to ensure the delivery of high quality services.

Each Contractor has an 'Annual Contract Value' paid in 12 equal monthly instalments. This is a payment for providing primary dental services, as agreed, at the practice address. However, it is often interpreted, both by dentists and PCTs, as payment for a given number of Units of Dental Activity (UDAs). From this payment the Contractor must pay the expenses of the practice, both fixed and variable as well as reimbursement for all Performers (dentists) in the practice.

♦ Chapter 8, 'Services & courses of treatment', p 82.

More recently new contracts have been set up which recognise more than UDAs, such as payments for Key Performance Indicators (KPIs) and for seeing patients new to the practice.

Performers (associates) do not receive any of this 'Annual Contract Value' as of right, but are paid in accordance with the contract they have with their practice owners. This may be based on payment for each UDA submitted. They are are automatically members of the NHS pension scheme unless they opt out.

There are also payments for specific purposes:

- payments for domiciliary and sedation services paid to the Contractor
- seniority payments – paid to dentists over the age of 55 who fulfil certain criteria
- payments in connection with vocational training paid to vocational dental practitioner, trainer and the Contractor
- payments for maternity, paternity and adoption leave paid to the individual concerned
- payments for long-term sickness paid to individuals who fulfil certain criteria
- reimbursement of non-domestic rates, paid to the Contractor.

Performers

When a dentist goes to work in a practice after vocational training, they will almost invariably be an associate (Performer). If you are in this position you should have a written contract with your practice owner outlining your rights and responsibilities while you are working there.

Although not in contract with your local PCT, you are responsible for working within the NHS regulations. You will also have to be on a PCT's **Performers List**. You will also be expected to maintain your registration with the GDC, including participating in continuing professional development (CPD), and to provide your own professional indemnity.

Types of contract

There are two different types of contract to provide Primary Dental Services.

● **General Dental Services (GDS) Contract**

◗ 'Services', p 6.

This is the 'standard' contract to provide certain 'mandatory' services; it can also contain certain 'additional' services. These contracts are usually without a fixed term.

● **Personal Dental Services (PDS) Agreement**

PDS Agreements are for a fixed number of years, after which they have to be renegotiated, and are applicable in two different circumstances:

1) Where, prior to the introduction of the new contract, dentists worked under Personal Dental Services arrangements.

2) Where the full range of mandatory services is not provided, such as in orthodontic practices.

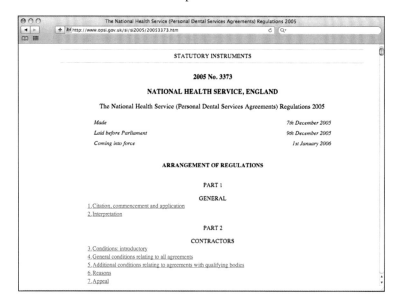

Figure 2: The online version of the PDS Agreement Regulations 2005, accessed via the Primary Care Contracting website (see below).

A new type of PDS Agreement, **Personal Dental Services Plus** (PDS+), was set up in 2009 by the Dental Access Team to improve access to services:

'Personal Dental Services Plus Agreement', Chief Dental Officer November 2009.

> **To ensure we improve people's access to NHS dentistry, we have developed a template agreement that PCTs can use to commission new services.**

The Regulations

The contract is governed by various regulations and directions. These can best be found on the NHS Primary Care Contracting website, as well as guidance and advice sheets. The main regulations and directions that will concern you can all be downloaded. They are as follows:

Figure 3: NHS Primary Care Contracting website (www.pcc.nhs. uk/). Click on 'Dentistry' in the left-hand column – within that there is a special section for 'Legislation, Regulation and Directions'.

- *GDS Regulations – The National Health Service (General Dental Services Contracts) Regulations 2005*
- *PDS Regulations – The National Health Service (Personal Dental Services Agreements) Regulations 2005*
- *The National Health Service (Performers Lists) Regulations 2004* – in order to practise dentistry under the NHS you need to be on a 'Performers List' with a PCT
- *The National Health Service (Dental Charges) Regulations 2005* and *The National Health Service (Dental Charges) Amendment Regulations 2006* – these set out what charges you can collect
- *The GDS and PDS Statements of Financial Entitlements* – these cover the amount paid to the practice (the Annual Contract Value) and payments for specific purposes including vocational training and maternity.

Another useful source for the regulations and guidance on the contract is the Chief Dental Officer's site on the Department of Health website.

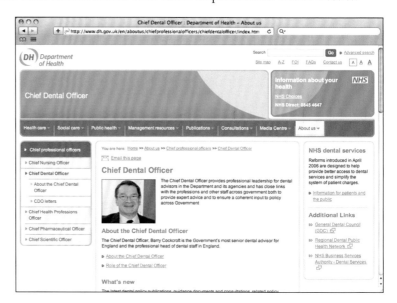

Figure 4: Website of the Chief Dental Officer (www.dh.gov.uk/en/aboutus/chiefprofessionalofficers/chiefdentalofficer/index.htm).

Variations and change of practice owner

▶ 'UDAs and targets', p 7.

The PCT and Contractor can agree variations for most parts of the contract: for instance, the level of service (including number of UDAs), the contract value, opening hours, and so on. If there is no agreement the PCT can impose changes, provided it has a valid reason for doing this. The dentist can appeal against an unreasonable decision.

But if the Contractor leaves and no longer holds the contract, then a new one has to be negotiated with the new owner. Dentists have every right to sell their practices but no right to pass on their NHS contract. Where a practice is being sold, it is for the PCT to decide whether or not to offer a new contract, but it needs to consider the importance of continuity of services.

Services

The services you offer your patients can be divided into **mandatory services** and **additional services**. Mandatory services are described as the care and treatment which 'a dental practitioner usually undertakes for a patient and which the patient is willing to undergo' and, where appropriate, the referral of the patient to a hospital or other dentist.

There are five types of additional services; you can only offer these if this is written into your contract.

1) **Advanced mandatory services**
2) **Dental public health services**

3) **Domiciliary services**
4) **Orthodontic services**
5) **Sedation services**

The term 'advanced mandatory services' needs some explanation. They are some mandatory services (as defined above) which you cannot personally provide because you do not possess the particular 'high level of facilities, experience or expertise' which they need. They are provided on referral to another dentist, who must have the provision of them written into their contract.

◆ Chapter 8, 'Services & courses of treatment', p 87.

Specialties and referrals

Referral into secondary care is well established in the profession, but less so referral to another dentist in primary care, except in areas such as orthodontics, sedation and implants. Written into the 2006 contract is the intention that you should be able to refer patients within primary rather than secondary care. This is also preferable for PCTs, as the costs would be lower.

If you wish to provide orthodontics and sedation, these must be commissioned in your contract. Some PCTs have set up facilities for oral surgery referrals, but such services are in their infancy. The same applies to the new Dentists with Special Interest initiative. **Dentists with Special Interests** were established in May 2004, so that practitioners who had expertise in areas such as orthodontics, oral surgery, endodontics and periodontology could be recognised by their PCT and accept referrals from others.

◆ Chapter 4, 'The dental team working together', p 42.

UDAs and targets

The **Unit of Dental Activity** (UDA) is one of the most talked-about but misunderstood parts of the 2006 contract. UDAs are courses of treatment weighted according to their complexity, so a course of treatment involving laboratory work attracts 12 UDAs, whereas one comprising only an examination is for 1 UDA. They are supposed to be an indication of activity, not an item of service.

The content of a course of treatment may vary from practice to practice. For example, one practice may have patients who require only 'maintenance' care – such as the occasional filling or more rarely an extraction or a crown – while another practice may have patients who need multiple fillings, crowns or dentures.

What applies to a course of treatment applies to the content of a UDA. Their value was set by reference to a 'test year'. In that year the first practice in the example above would have done more courses of treatment with less content. The second practice would have done fewer courses of treatment but with more content. Consequently the first practice would have a low UDA value and the second practice a higher one. This disparity

◆ Chapter 11, 'Monitoring your contract, p 126.

of UDA values has been criticised in various reports and many PCTs are working towards equalising them across their area.

Patients and 'registration'

◆ Chapter 6, 'Patients', p 56.

There is no registration of patients as in the previous contract, but many practices maintain lists of 'their' patients. Some PCTs maintain waiting lists of those requiring treatment; they also have targets of improving on the numbers seen within the previous two years. At the time of the new contract in 2006 the Government recognised the significance still attached to the term 'registration', and promised to 'examine the scope and options for some form of registration'. In opposition, the Conservatives pledged to base a new contract on registration.

Government response to Health Select Committee report on Dental Services: Cm 7470, October 2008.

Ⓡ S3 C 1(4)

Once you have completed treatment, in contract terms they are no longer your patients and you are under no obligation to see them again, but most practices continue to see their 'regular' patients. Unless your contract specifies that you are to treat a specific group of people, you must not refuse to see anyone on various grounds including 'medical or dental condition'. This means that you cannot turn away a patient who needs extensive treatment.

2 SETTING THE SCENE

The reports discussed and the ideas they had in common are summarised in tabular form as the Annex to this chapter. pp 17–19.

'Report of the Tattersall Committee'. *BDJ*, October 1964, pp 299–345.

Dental Strategy Review Group Report. Department of Health, 1981.

Schanschieff (1986).

Proposals for reform, 1964–2010

There have been calls for reform of NHS dentistry, almost since it started in 1948. In 1964 the British Dental Association published the Tattersall Report, which identified shortcomings of the existing system. Many of these continue to be relevant today, including:

- no financial recognition to the profession for increasing productivity
- a premium on speed of working, with no account taken of quality
- the system of averaging, which led to the 'treadmill' and took no account of different levels of expenses.

The Dental Strategy Review Group in 1981 also identified shortcomings in the service. These included the failure to prevent avoidable disease; inequality in the distribution of services, and the inability of some of the population to obtain adequate dental care because of disability, old age or social disadvantage.

The Committee of Inquiry into Unnecessary Dental Treatment was set up in 1984 and two years later produced a report usually referred to as the Schanschieff Report, after its Chairman. It said that, overall, unnecessary treatment was significant but concluded that an 'out of date treatment philosophy' might be a primary cause of this, rather than deliberate abuse. They considered the suggestion that item of service payments encouraged dentists to over-treat; one suggested solution was a change to capitation. They also questioned whether the fee scale gave too much weight to restorative rather than preventive treatment. Much of this thinking was carried forward into the 2006 contract, twenty years later.

The 1990 contract and consequences

The October 1990 contract was the first major change since 1948. The changes brought in capitation payments for children and continuing care payments for adult patients. There was widespread opposition to its introduction, and for many dentists it started their disenchantment with NHS dentistry.

Equally significant was the fee cut in 1992. This was followed by a fundamental review of the system under Sir Kenneth Bloomfield, the former head of the Northern Ireland Civil Service. This produced some more radical thinking. In the short term, he recommended what he called 'bulk payments' – in effect, capitation payments. While Government recognised that there was no evidence for a drop in quality, it accepted that, in the main,

Report of Sir Kenneth Bloomfield: Fundamental Review of Dental Remuneration. Department of Health, December 2002.

> **any perverse incentives derive from the basis of payment by fee for item of service. The incentives to high throughput of patients and restorative work for high earnings could not be removed without the replacement of that system.**

Para 58, *Improving NHS Dentistry,* July 1994 (CM 2625)

In the longer term Bloomfield wanted consideration to be given to more radical options, such as moving to a more locally sensitive or even devolved system of administration, or replacing the remuneration system with a range of options which could be adapted to local use.

The House of Commons Health Committee also considered the system and reported in 1993. It endorsed the need to encourage everybody to see their dentist regularly. There was also a need for prompt treatment for patients in pain. It endorsed the new philosophy of replacing the emphasis on dental treatment with one of prevention through continuing care. It also looked at oral health inequalities and the need to focus services on the more vulnerable sections to population.

House of Commons Health Committee, Fourth Report of Session 1992–93, *Dental Services*, HC 264–I.

The Committee produced the following recommendations.

- There should be a core service of diagnostic and preventive care available free to all patients and paid for through capitation, banded in relation to the patient's oral health.
- Treatment necessary to secure dental fitness prior to registration should be remunerated through item of service.
- There should be a maximum list size for each practice.
- There should be an independent dental inspectorate controlled nationally but utilised locally.
- The Department of Health should negotiate a laboratory fee scale for laboratory treatments and the resulting scale fees should be paid without deduction by the dentist to the laboratory.

Improving NHS Dentistry. Department of Health, July 1994 (CM 2625).

In 1994 the Government published a white paper, *Improving NHS Dentistry*, which took on board the recommendations of both the Bloomfield and Health Committee reports. The main recommendation was to set up a local system along the lines of the purchaser-Provider model current in the rest of the NHS. An Act of Parliament was passed in the dying days of the Conservative administration for pilots to be set up under a scheme, which became known as Personal Dental Services.

Modernising NHS dentistry

Modernising NHS Dentistry: Implementing the NHS Plan. Department of Health, September 2000.

In September 2000, the Labour Government published its strategy document for modernising NHS dentistry. The major proposals concerned improvement to access and better oral health, with increasing responsibilities for health authorities. It focused mainly on improving access for unregistered patients seeking immediate treatment, and included an expansion of the role for NHS Direct and access centres. No changes to the system of remuneration were suggested, although there were doubts about the suitability of fees for examinations, scaling and some orthodontic treatments.

Access to NHS Dentistry. Select Committee on Health Report, March 2001.

The next year the House of Commons Health Committee held a short inquiry, which concentrated almost exclusively on access to NHS dentistry. It found that that the GDS remuneration system was at the heart of the access problem, with the fee structure encouraging the move of dentists out of the NHS and discouraging preventive care. The Committee also felt that the role of health authorities was not clear and they did not possess the levers they needed to meet the objectives of the strategy.

Figure 5: *NHS Dentistry: Options for Change*. Department of Health, August 2002.

Dentistry: primary dental services in England and Wales: Audit commission 2002.

Options for Change

The stage was set for yet another report, *Options for Change*, which set out many of the ideas and principles behind the 2006 changes. A key proposal in the report was for a new PCT-led dental service, responsive to local need. The proposed service should integrate services currently provided under the GDS, Personal Dental Services and Community Dental Services to focus on preventive measures to combat dental disease and to tackle serious oral health inequalities, particularly in children. The paper also recommended that treatment options should be evidence-based and patient-focused, and that patient charges, then totalling over 400 individual items, should be simplified.

Following *Options for Change*, the Audit Commission published its report on primary dental services, drawing on many of the previously published reports. Its conclusions included the following:

- The NHS should emphasise prevention. Much health promotion activity is best done by local health commissioning bodies but the Government should act to secure rapid fluoridation of water supplies.

- The piecework system should be replaced. A new national framework should enable patients who are at high risk of decay and gum disease to receive more frequent check-ups than those with generally good oral health. The NHS should define what it will pay for, and the standards expected from primary care dental services should also be made clear. Cosmetic activities should not be paid for by the NHS. The charging system should be reviewed to ensure that people who are on lower incomes are not deterred from seeking necessary dental healthcare.

- Local health commissioning bodies should shape services in order to achieve national standards and to secure fair access through local contracts with dentists.

The Health and Social Care Act 2003

The legislation that enabled these changes to be introduced was included in the Health and Social Care Act which became law in November 2003. The changes came into effect on 1 April 2006. PCTs were given a legal obligation to commission primary dental care:

> **Each Primary Care Trust and Local Health Board must, to the extent that it considers necessary to meet all reasonable requirements, exercise its powers so as to provide primary dental services within its area, or to secure their provision within its area.**

Health and Social Care (Community Health and Standards) Act 2003. Part 4 Para 170.

The word 'reasonable' is not precisely defined and depends on the prevailing circumstances. A PCT is a public body and the reasonableness of any of its decisions when exercising its statutory duties is subject to scrutiny and legal challenge through judicial review.

PCTs are responsible for assessing local oral health needs and addressing them. The emphasis will be on preventive care and improving quality and access. PCTs also have responsibility for dental public health.

PCTs have been given directly allocated financial resources to commission dental services to meet local needs and are responsible for commissioning out-of-hours services from interested dental practices. NHS dentists are paid an agreed contract value for meeting patients' reasonable requirements, rather than on an item of service basis.

Consultation on the draft National Health Service (Dental Charges) Regulations 2006. (GR 5092). Department of Health.

The Act also provided for a new regime for patient charges for dental treatment. The proposed changes to this were published for consultation in July 2005. The three banded treatment charges were laid before Parliament in December 2005 and became effective on 1 April 2006.

Department of Health's proposals 2004

In February 2004, framework proposals for primary dental services in England were published and consultations undertaken with the profession. This document set out the Department of Health's proposals and sought to explain them to dentists in primary dental care. It also gave an outline of the so-called 'base contract' which could be used locally during transition into the new system.

Framework proposals for primary dental services in England from 2005. Department of Health, March 2004.

The profession was unenthusiastic about these proposals and the Government twice postponed the start date from April 2005 to October 2005 and then again to April 2006. Difficulties were also encountered agreeing the terms of a Base Contract – a default contract for all those prac-

2: Setting the scene

NHS Dentistry: Delivering Change.
Chief Dental Officer. DHG Ref 3497
(July 2004).

tices who had not agreed a contract with their PCTs. Practices and PCTs were encouraged to establish personal dental services under a scheme established under the National Health Service (Primary Care) Act 1997 contracts, prior to the introduction of the new system. These were pilots: PCTs were assisted in commissioning these services by a Department of Health team that scrutinised all the bids, many of which were agreed on the basis of increasing access to NHS services locally. The principles were set out in two key documents from the Department of Health in August 2004:

- *NHS Dentistry: Next Steps in Local Commissioning* (GR 3571)
- *Personal Dental Services – A Step By Step Guide.*

Despite the enthusiasm with which the profession took up the PDS contracting arrangements – when a third of practices signed up to PDS – further approval to establish more pilots ceased after a written ministerial statement from Rosie Winterton MP on 7 July 2005. This decision to end the pilots was in part due to the drop in activity and thus patient charge revenue collection over and above that of the expected 10–15 per cent drop seen in earlier PDS pilots.

Hansard: HC Deb 7 Jul 2005:
Column 16WS.

National Audit Office 2004

In November 2004, the National Audit Office reported on its risk management assessment of the proposed new contract. It highlighted many of the issues that have arisen since its implementation.

It said that part of the Department's rationale for changing NHS dentistry is to 'encourage dentists to maintain and increase their NHS commitments'. But given the 'scepticism of some dentists compounded by a lack of detail on how the new system will operate there is a risk that dentists will reduce their NHS commitments'. This indeed applied to about 10 per cent of dentists, but only 3 per cent of output. The report also noted that as dentists were being guaranteed gross earnings for three years, the risk would continue through the transition and might not materialise until the end of the period. (This guaranteed earnings period was later extended to five years.)

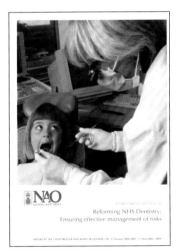

Figure 6: *Reforming NHS Dentistry: Ensuring effective management of risks.* Report by The Comptroller and Auditor General, HC 25 Session 2004-2005, 25 November 2004. National Audit Office.

Contracts, the report said, must make clear what is to be delivered and who is accountable. All Primary Care Trusts would need to analyse dentists' broad patterns of working by numbers of patients treated under the NHS taking account of complexity of treatment:

'Summary', ¶c, p 9.

> Unless there are clear incentives for dentists to extend access and take on socially disadvantaged patients, there is a risk that freed up capacity potentially flowing from more flexible recall periods and changes in the methods of working may not be used effectively for the NHS.

It continued:

> In moving away from piece work systems, there is a risk of 'under treatment' replacing 'over treatment' as a perverse incentive. The Department will need to monitor national data and sample the quality of care provided to ensure this does not happen. Equally, the Department and Primary Care Trusts will need to establish effective clinical audit and evidenced based quality assurance arrangements, and disseminate lessons.

'Summary', ¶d, p 9.

The report suggested that income from patient charges may fall. With a move towards prevention, there was a risk that treatment patterns may affect the overall level of charge income. The Department, together with the newly-created NHS Business Services Authority (BSA), would need to develop a system to monitor overall charges to ensure that it continued to recover a similar contribution towards the overall cost of NHS dentistry.

It concluded that, although data on dentistry had been collected for many years, the evidence base did not provide conclusive answers to issues such as the appropriateness of the recall period, how accessible NHS dental services were, and what role dentistry plays in promoting oral health. The Department would need to review its data requirements to ensure that available data could support further research on cost effectiveness.

Health Committee 2008

House of Commons, Health Committee, Dental Services, Fifth Report of Session 2007–08, released 2 July 2008.

The House of Commons Health Committee held an inquiry and reported in 2008 on the contract, which it said was failing to improve dental services, as assessed by the Department of Health's own criteria for success. Despite assertions from the Chief Dental Officer that the situation had stabilised and improvements would soon be seen, access to dentistry remained uneven across the country; indications were that the new arrangements were failing on the whole to improve patient access.

The report made a number of recommendations:

- Improve PCT commissioning by developing in-house skills and by drawing on advice from dental public health specialists.
- Base future PCT dental funding on a local needs assessment, not on a historic basis.
- Review the Units of Dental Activity (UDA) system so dentists are rewarded for providing appropriate treatment.
- Consider introducing a Quality and Outcomes Framework (QOF)-style reward system for dentists who improve the dental health of their patients.
- Reinstate patient registration to improve dentist-patient relationship.
- Ensure changes to the system are piloted and tested rigorously.

The Committee found it extraordinary that the new remuneration system for dentists, based on UDAs, was not piloted or tested before it was introduced in 2006. Too many PCTs had set unrealistic UDA targets; a more flexible approach must be adopted. The CDO appeared to argue that if PCTs and dentists acted more flexibly and used common sense and goodwill, the new arrangements would work. The Committee saw little evidence that this would happen.

The number of complex treatments involving laboratory work had fallen by 50 per cent during the first year of the contract. The reason for the decline had not been satisfactorily explained and the report raised concerns that some patients did not receive the quality of care they needed within the NHS. The Department, the report said, must publish an explanation for this trend and commission research into the effect of this decline within the NHS system and its impact on oral health.

Many dentists feared an exodus from the General Dental Service in 2009 once guaranteed income ended, although the Department had claimed no such exodus would occur. The Committee urged the Department to monitor closely the career plans of NHS dentists.

The guaranteed income period was extended to 2011. Between 2006/07 and 2009/10 the number of dentists with NHS activity rose from 20,160 to 22,003, (NHS Infomation Centre: NHS Dental Statistics for England: 2009/10).

The report welcomed the Department's decision to analyse how dental services might develop over the next five years and called on the Department to address the extent to which NHS dentistry should offer the growing number of treatments which do not address clinical ill-health but are concerned with improving the quality of life.

Professor Jimmy Steele's review

At the end of 2008, in response to the Health Committee's report, the Department of Health asked Professor Jimmy Steele to carry out an independent review of NHS dental services in England. He reported back in June 2009. The Government accepted his reported recommendations in principle, including proposals that changes should be piloted first before being rolled out across the country.

His main recommendations were as follows.

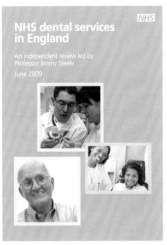

Figure 7: *NHS Dental Services in England – An independent review led by Professor Jimmy Steele.* Department of Health June 2009.

- NHS dentistry should be commissioned and delivered around a staged pathway through care, which would allow and encourage continuity of the relationship between patients and dentists, for those who want it, built around the most appropriate recall interval for the patient and using oral health as an outcome.
- Patients registered in a continuing care relationship with a practice should have an absolute right to return to that practice for both routine and urgent care.
- Urgent care services should be accessible and commissioned to a high and consistent level of quality.

- Strong clinical guidelines should be developed to support dentists and patients through specific pathways of treatment. These would allow determination of thresholds for treatment, ensuring that some of the costly and complex care can be targeted to the patients where it will provide greatest benefit.
- The free replacement period for restorations should be extended to three years; the Provider should bear the full cost of replacement rather than the PCT or the patient.

On aligning the contract to improve access and quality the review recommended that:

- Dental contracts are developed with much clearer incentives for improving health, improving access and improving quality.
- The current contract should be developed specifically to allow payments for continuing care responsibility, blended with rewards for both activity and quality. (He further recommended for these to be piloted and then nationally applied.)
- An annual per person registration payment to dentists should be introduced within the contract.
- The quality of a service and the outcomes it achieves should be explicitly recognised in the reward system of the revised contract.
- A high priority should be given to developing a consistent set of quality measures.

White Paper 2010

◗ Preface, p x.

In July 2010, the Coalition Government produced an NHS White Paper for England, *Equity and excellence: Liberating the NHS*. This promised a new contract for dentists:

¶3.22.

> Following consultation and piloting, we will introduce a new dentistry contract, with a focus on improving quality, achieving good dental health and increasing access to NHS dentistry, and an additional focus on the oral health of schoolchildren.

It also proposed the abolition of Primary Care Trusts and Strategic Health Authorities by 2013. Commissioning for secondary care will be through GP consortia, but primary care dentistry will be commissioned by a new NHS Commissioning Board.

The chart below summarises the main threads in attempts to reform NHS dentistry over the past 50 years and the effect of the 2006 contract on their achievement.

Thread	Proposal	Action
Local commissioning	Every report since the early 1990s has recommended that the management of NHS dentistry should be put in the hands of local health bodies, which should have funds allocated to them to provide or commission primary dental services.	The *2003 Act* gave local health bodies the duty to provide or commission services and authorised the allocation of funds to them. Local commissioning is seen by the Government as pivotal to the contract.
The Item of Service system	Defects in the system were first identified by *Tattersall* in 1964 and since then most reports have advocated its abolition. It was seen as encouraging over-prescription and having a 'treadmill' effect.	Item of Service was abolished in the *2006 contract*, although many regard the new system as having introduced just four bands of treatment each with a UDA value. Some feel that over-prescription has been replaced by neglect and that the treadmill effect still persists.
Alternatives to Item of Service system	Capitation is the favoured alternative among reports, although a sessional payment system and a revised fee scale have been suggested (and the latter implemented in Scotland).	An element of capitation was introduced in the *1990 contract*. Capitation for children and continuing care payments for adults were abolished by the *2006 contract*, removing all vestiges of capitation from the new system, although the *Steele Review* recommends its re-introduction. The concept of an Annual Contract Value is totally new and no report recommended it.
Activity monitoring	Most reports advocate the abolition of item of service payments and with this an effective monitoring system. There is little agreement on what should replace it, although the favoured capitation systems point towards numbers of registered patients.	The ending of both item of service payments and registration removed two indicators of activity and the only one left is number of courses of treatment, weighted according to complexity – the unit of dental activity (UDA). In reality the UDA has become almost the sole indicator of activity and has, in effect, reintroduced item of service but with only four items. More recently different indicators have been introduced to some contracts, such as Key Performance Indicators.

Thread	Proposal	Action
Separation of expenses	Both *Bloomfield* and the *1993 Health Committee* recommended that expenses, especially laboratory fees, should be paid differently and perhaps reimbursed directly. The *Audit Commission* made similar recommendations in 2003.	Capital payments have been introduced and PCTs given power to 'assist' practices financially. The Annual Contract Value is paid to cover all expenses, including laboratory fees and associates' payments, both of which can be reduced with an increase in practice profit.
What treatments should be available in NHS dentistry?	*Options for Change* and the subsequent *Audit Commission* report advocated the development of clinical pathways to identify appropriate evidence-based treatments. Other treatments, often cosmetic in nature, should not be provided under the NHS.	The only care pathway so far identified is the Oral Health Assessment, but not formally incorporated into the *2006 contract*. There are no clear guidelines as to what does or does not constitute treatment appropriate to the NHS.
Career development	Under the old contract there was little career development for general dental practitioners. Every dentist was considered equal in terms of payment for items of service. One year's vocational training was introduced during the 1980s. Seniority payments were introduced to recompense older dentists whose output was declining.	There has been little change. Vocational training continues with some moves towards extending this to two years. Seniority payments were to have been reviewed to reward experience, but this has not yet happened. There is no equivalent career structure as there is in general medical practice.
Specialist care	Specialist care was, in the main, regarded as in the province of secondary care and there were few proposals for its reform, except in the field of orthodontics where an Index of Orthodontic Treatment Need (IOTN) was proposed.	The IOTN and other quality measures have been introduced into orthodontics. In general dentistry treatment on referral, through 'advanced mandatory services', was to be encouraged and Dentists with Special Interests were to be appointed. There is little sign of this happening generally.
Oral health inequalities	Most reports have stressed the need to reduce oral health inequalities.	Local commissioning was supposed to address this by placing on PCTs the responsibility for carrying out a local needs assessment and commissioning to reduce inequalities. Some PCTs are developing such an approach in a systematic manner.

Annex: Attempts to reform NHS dentistry since 1960

Thread	Proposal	Action
Prevention	Most reports also express the intention to move away from 'drill and fill' towards a preventive based service. The consensus view was that the delivery of prevention was not possible under the old arrangements.	The Department of Health published a toolkit for prevention in the autumn of 2007. However many dentists argue that prevention is still not possible under the new arrangements.
Quality	Most reports have also stressed the need to improve and monitor quality. This was the responsibility of the old Dental Practice Board and doubts were expressed as to its effectiveness.	Responsibility for maintaining high standards and quality now lies with PCTs, who have begun to address this issue. The Dental Reference Service has been given new responsibilities to monitor practices. Since April 2008 PCTs have been able to access data that tells them what items each Performer is providing within their units of dental activity. This should enable them to identify those dentists who are not providing necessary treatment.

3 COMMISSIONING

In order to understand how dentistry will fit into the overall NHS framework it is useful to take a look at the structure of the NHS as it stands now, and what it will probably look like after 2013 (Figure 8). At present budgets and responsibility pass down from Parliament to the Department of Health to Strategic Health Authorities to Primary Care Trusts. The latter are responsible for commissioning services from dentists and managing contracts. The structure from 2013 is subject to legislation and further discussion, but the likely structure is that primary dental services will be commissioned by the NHS Commissioning Board. Local Authorities will have a role promoting the joining up of local NHS services, social care and health improvement.

Figure 8: Left, the current structure of the NHS (adapted from *The Structure of the NHS*, Royal College of General Practitioners, Information Sheet No 8); right, the likely structure after 2013.

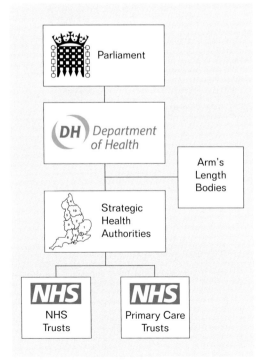

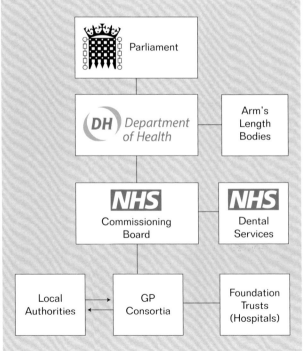

Dental functions of PCTs

Dental Contract Management Handbook.
January 2010 (GR 12589). Department
of Health.

Since April 2006, PCTs have had responsibility for commissioning primary dental services to reflect local needs and priorities. This includes agreeing and monitoring local contracts with dentists or corporate bodies for the delivery of primary dental services. PCTs must assess local needs and demand and deciding how these can be addressed. They must also collect information on the quality of the services provided, so that they can manage performance, support quality improvements and provide information for patients and the public. They must manage dentists' contracts through a system of annual and mid-year reviews. PCTs must manage the dental Performer list. They also have the responsibility for the management of the overall dental budget within the PCT, including supervision of dental patient charge revenue. It remains to be seen how these functions will be carried out in the new system.

Arm's length bodies

The Department of Health's arm's length bodies were reviewed in 2010. These are organisations that are financed by and accountable to Parliament or the Department, but are not part of it. Those that relate to dentistry are shown in Table 1.

Body	Present function	Future
Care Quality Commission	Took over functions of Healthcare Commission, Commission for Social Care Inspection and Mental Health Act Commission.	It will be registering dental practices, NHS, private and mixed; it will require them to ensure that complaints are responded to effectively.
Council for Healthcare Regulatory Excellence	Regulates other regulators such as General Dental Council.	To become self-funding through a levy on those it regulates.
National Institute of Health and Clinical Excellence (NICE)	Produces guidance on drugs and techniques, e.g. dental recall interval.	To continue with enhanced role.
National Patient Safety Agency	Co-ordinates improvement in patient safety.	To be abolished.
Health Protection Agency	Radiological protection.	To be part of new Public Health Service.
NHS Litigation Authority	Acts as an appeal body for contract disputes.	To be subject to a commercial review.
NHS Business Services Authority (Dental Services)	Payment of dentists.	To be subject to a commercial review.

Table 1: Arm's length bodies.

Challenges for the NHS

The Coalition Government's NHS reforms: an assessment of the White Paper. August 2010. The Nuffield Trust. www.nuffieldtrust.org.uk/publications

Commissioning in a cold climate. The NHS Confederation Issue. 5 June 2009.

The NHS is facing a major financial challenge. Official NHS sources suggest that, to meet rising demand, there will be a funding shortfall between 2011 and 2014 of £15 to £20 billion. Given the extent of the anticipated downturn in public spending, it seems inevitable that commissioners must reconsider the scale, pace and methods of change required to achieve objectives.

Commissioners are constrained in primary care to reduce their expenditure since the core costs of GMS (General Medical Services) and GDS contracts cannot be reduced locally unilaterally, even if practices are able to work more efficiently and reduce their own operating costs. What is clear, however, is that the future for commissioning will look very different to what it was.

The biggest change brought about by the 2006 Contract was the interdependent relationship between an NHS dentist and the local PCT. In a very real sense, the PCT, as the commissioner of a local dental service, was a dentist's new 'customer'. In common with developing any sales relationship, the following factors apply:

- knowledge and understanding
- honesty
- trust
- communication
- openness
- respect.

The first prerequisites of fostering a relationship are knowing who the customer is, what it is they want from you and whether you will be able to deliver what they want at the price they are willing to pay.

That relationship will change now that PCTs are due to be abolished by 2013. The first change will be that commissioning will be carried out by the National Commissioning Board via regional offices.

The second change, somewhat subtler, will be in the relationship a practice has with their PCT over the next three years, as the lights go out in the Trust. Morale amongst PCT officers is sure to deteriorate and, as the changes to the personnel take place, there will be less engagement with practices. This may have both positive and negative effects for practices. Those that have had a good ongoing relationship with committed and enlightened PCT managers will regret the changes, while many others may feel the involvement of their PCT in their affairs since 2006 has been less than helpful. There are challenges for practices to build new relations with the NHS Commissioning Board.

Relationship building

The key to the success of the current contracting arrangements lies in the inter-relationship between the PCT and the practices. Figure 9 shows four possible approaches a practice could take.

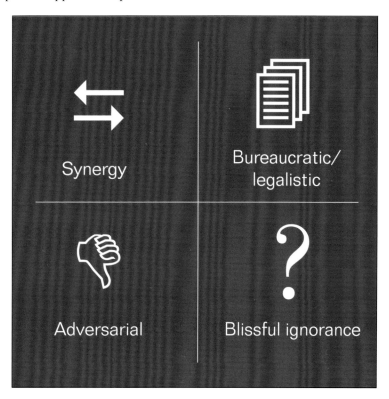

Figure 9: Possible approaches for a dental practice.

An *adversarial* approach was characteristic of the pre-2006 contract, and dentists and their legal advisers could afford to take a *bureaucratic and legalistic* approach to their relationship with commissioners. If a dentist won a disciplinary committee hearing on a technicality or a complaint was ruled out of time because he or she applied the rules very strictly, the only victor was the dentist. In the 2006 system, winning technical arguments about the interpretation of contract clauses or denying patients care on capacity grounds may be legally right but may not necessarily be in the spirit of the contract. If a practice that does this also receives several complaints which it handles badly, the commissioner may be less likely to commission services from that practice in the future.

Failing to engage in the commissioner's agenda and remaining *blissfully ignorant* of the changes – and the need, for example, to refocus clinical care according to NICE guidelines – will not foster the type of relationship that is now necessary in the new contracting arrangements.

The most appropriate relationship is one based on *synergy* where both parties to the contract collaborate together to deliver each other's short-

and long-term objectives. For this to happen, both parties need to communicate with each other, to be proactive rather than reactive and to ensure each party has the appropriate knowledge, attitude, skills and resources to deliver the agreed services. In such a relationship, if a practice wants to deliver a higher proportion of private care, the commissioner will be sufficiently mature and pragmatic to accept this and ought to work with the practice to ensure that those patients who do not wish to take up private services are offered NHS care with another Provider. A practice working synergistically with its commissioner will deliver on the clinical governance and quality assurance agendas, ensure patients' complaints are minimised – but handled professionally when they do occur – and where possible assist the commissioner in improving access to NHS services.

The culture of commissioning organisations and practices is different. It is difficult to analyse because values and beliefs are not always explicit and can change when there are changes in leadership and reorganisations of the structures. One qualitative method is to use the Competing Values model which has been applied to healthcare organisations. It comprises two dimensions.

The first dimension is process-centred and the second relates the organisation to the outside world. The resulting matrix, shown in Figure 10, describes four cultures:

- clan
- developmental
- hierarchical
- rational.

Cameron *et al.* (1991).

Figure 10: Competing Values model of culture types for organisations (taken from Marshall *et al* (2003) and adapted from Cameron *et al.* (1991)).

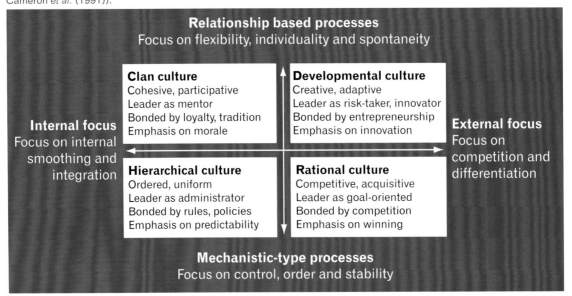

Relationship based processes
Focus on flexibility, individuality and spontaneity

Internal focus
Focus on internal smoothing and integration

Clan culture
Cohesive, participative
Leader as mentor
Bonded by loyalty, tradition
Emphasis on morale

Developmental culture
Creative, adaptive
Leader as risk-taker, innovator
Bonded by entrepreneurship
Emphasis on innovation

External focus
Focus on competition and differentiation

Hierarchical culture
Ordered, uniform
Leader as administrator
Bonded by rules, policies
Emphasis on predictability

Rational culture
Competitive, acquisitive
Leader as goal-oriented
Bonded by competition
Emphasis on winning

Mechanistic-type processes
Focus on control, order and stability

Most organisations, including your practice, will have elements of all types but it is likely that one culture will dominate. As you get to know your commissioning team, it is valuable to understand the culture. It will facilitate your relationship-building and make you more effective in your dealings and negotiations with the managers.

In a study on the management of change in general medical practice, PCT managers reported that change would be difficult to deliver

> unless practices change their culture to one that valued greater collaboration [...] and a willingness to be more flexible in the way that they operated.

(The PCT managers who were questioned had certain perceptions about general medical practice, many of which we believe would apply to general dental practice.)

In recent research professional relationships between primary care organisations and practitioners were generally described as good. However, where conflict was experienced, dental public health consultants cited relations with local dental committees (LDCs) as an area of concern. Many consider in any case that LDCs are highly political and some doubt their effectiveness in representing the views of the wider GDP community.

Holmes et al. (2008)

Working with commissioning managers

Studies have shown that two styles of management dominate at commissioning level, **directive** and **facilitative**. Comparisons between these two styles are summarised below.

	Directive managers	Facilitative managers
Approach	Revolution: challenge established values	Evolution: work with established values
Focus	Performance targets	Gaining trust, building relationships
Incentives	External, especially financial	Internal, especially protected time
Levers	Patients or the public Executive position Political authority	Practice managers and practice nurses
Use of peers	Peer competition	Peer support
Perceptions of obstacles to cultural change	Individual blockers	Organisations or environmental impediments

Table 2: Comparison between directive and facilitative managers (taken from Marshall *et al.* (2003)).

The directive style is more common among senior managers than middle managers; middle managers favour the facilitative approach. The relationship between Providers and managers is one of the critical success factors. Dentists did not need to foster these relations in the past, but need to do so now. In most cases, Providers are dealing with middle managers who act as a buffer between the clinicians and the senior team. Assuming you are the Contractor, your own management style will need to complement that of the managers with whom you will be discussing your contractual affairs. These will include finance and capital grants, performance management issues, matters arising from the mid-year review, your vision and growth strategy, and a host of other patient-related issues.

It may sometimes be appropriate to deal directly with senior management if you are not achieving the results you want, particularly if your problems are the sort which impact on the levers that give incentive to directive-style managers, such as patient service or performance figures.

The success or failure of the contract will depend on your ongoing relationship with the commissioners. Whatever your commitment to the NHS, your ability to survive and thrive within it in the coming years will depend on your adaptability and your understanding of what is important to the commissioner, whether a PCT or the NHS Commissioning Board.

Commissioning services

The early years of the NHS contract can be looked at as dominated by 'local contracting'. After 2009, however, the role of the PCT was to commission services and this 'local commissioning' is likely to play an increasing role in the future.

Ring-fencing

The full NHS dental budget was devolved to PCTs from April 2006 and for the first three years was 'ring-fenced'. This concept of 'floor funding' – below which dental spending is not allowed to drop – means that if a practitioner decides to reduce his NHS commitment, the lost capacity can be replaced by the PCT, either in the same practice or elsewhere. This ring-fencing was extended by two years until March 2011.

Announced by Minister, Ann Keen, in a Department of Health press release, 5 March 2008.

The Department of Health had also made it clear to PCTs that a ring-fenced budget meant that the money allocated on dentistry should be spent on commissioning and/or providing primary care services alone and that it must be spent by the end of each financial year, up to 31 March 2011. If the money was not spent by the PCT, the Department of Health and SHA would redeploy the funding elsewhere in the SHA area or, failing that, in another SHA. The message to PCTs was clear – spend it or lose it.

PCT Dentistry Budgets 2006–07 and patient charge income. Factsheet 4, ¶23 (GR 5917). Department of Health.

Increasingly, however, PCTs are not spending the ring-fenced budget on dentistry and allowing the underspent money to return to its global budget. Local practitioners and LDCs will only ever discover if this has happened in their own case by making applications, under the Freedom of Information Act 2000, to the Information Governance officer in their PCT.

From March 2011 Ministers must decide whether the ring-fencing will continue to apply or whether PCTs will be free to use their NHS dental budget in any way they feel appropriate. While legally they will still have an obligation to commission primary dental services, this function, and the relevant funding, will transfer to the NHS Commissioning Board. The real challenge for the profession comes when the 'ring-fenced' protected budget becomes unified with the commissioner's global budget. At that point primary dental care will be competing with possibly more emotive and serious priorities such as cancer management, coronary care, paediatric services and intensive care budgets. The situation will be exacerbated by the Government's need to make huge savings in public spending.

PCTs have a statutory duty to operate within their budgets, and most money given to PCTs – for example, Access Quality and Choice money or funding allocated for occupational health – disappears if not spent by the end of the financial year.

Most contracts with practices have been based on the test period and are effectively a like-for-like service.

Defining commissioning

Commissioning for health is the process by which the health needs of a population are assessed, responsibility is taken for ensuring that appropriate services are available which meet these needs and the accountability for the associated health outcome is established.

Health Reform in England: update in commissioning framework 2006 (GR 6865). Department of Health.

Commissioning has been defined as the means by which the NHS secures the best value for patients and taxpayers. 'Best value', in turn, is defined as:

- the best possible health outcome, including reducing health inequalities
- the best possible healthcare
- within the resources made available by the taxpayer.

Effective commissioning in dentistry makes the best use of allocated resources to achieve the following goals:

- Improve oral health and well being, reduce oral health inequalities and provide secure access to a comprehensive range of services.
- Improve the quality, effectiveness and efficiency of services.
- Increase choice for patients and ensure a better experience of dental care through greater responsiveness to people's needs.

Effective commissioning will also include access to emergency-out-of hours and urgent access.

From 2009 and beyond, commissioning can be divided up into four areas illustrated by the diagram below which will be discussed later on:

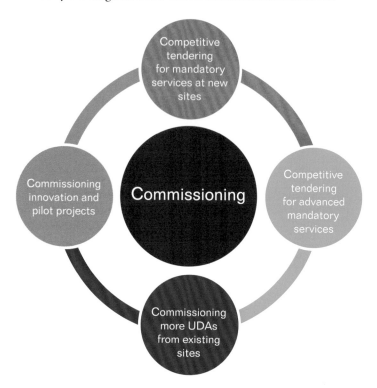

Figure 11: The structure of NHS local commissioning.

Best value for money and UDA values

The fundamental principle of commissioning is to ensure that the service provided is cost effective while still retaining quality standards. As with any commercial enterprise, different price points will deliver a variety of quality outcomes: ultimately it will be for the commissioner to decide how much they wish to pay for minimum quality standards.

As a result of the transition from old GDS Contracts to the new contract in April 2006 there is a wide variation of UDA values across a PCT. This effect may be further exaggerated by those PDS practices which converted to GDS practice in 2006 and were given higher values at the time.

The difference in UDA values between practices and between individual practitioners within the same practice was a result of differing patterns of treatment provision, reflecting:

- individual treatment philosophies
- demography of patient base
- workload and case mix.

New patients or irregular attenders requiring complex treatment ended up paying more, while existing stable patients seen for a long time by the same dentists generally paid less. The types of treatment these two groups of patients had was also different, with one having more intervention and the other more regular attenders having more prevention.

This resulted in quite legitimate variations in the price per UDA value that formed the basis of the like-for-like contract decision leading up to April 2006. These variations in cost per UDA still exist for the same valid reasons, but they make it difficult for PCTs to recommission new services at different rates across the PCT. While existing UDA values may persist, the commissioner now can only achieve value for money by commissioning new services at the average value for the area. A reasonable amendment to this approach would be to contract at higher UDA values when commissioning hard to reach groups or high needs patients, e.g. prison population, travellers or asylum seekers.

World Class Commissioning

DHG ref 5312 July 2005.

Out of *Commissioning a patient-led NHS* came the belief that the NHS should move from being a service that treated illness to one where the commissioning was focused on developing structures and processes to improve health and well being outcomes – in other words, World Class Commissioning (WCC).

WCC is underpinned by many existing processes such as practice-based commissioning for general medical practices, as well as services yet to be developed across health and social care.

The vision for WCC operates under the strap-line *Adding life to years and years to life* and has as its goals:

World Class Commissioning – Adding life to years and years to life December 2007 (GR 8754). Department of Health.

- **Better health and well being for all** –
  - people live healthier and longer lives
  - health inequalities are dramatically reduced.

- **Better care for all** –
  - services are evidence-based and of the best quality
  - people have choice and control over the services they use, so that those services become more personalised.

- **Better value for all** –
  - investment decisions are made in an informed and considered way, ensuring that improvements are delivered within available resources
  - PCTs work with others to optimise effective care.

Meeting the NHS operating framework objectives

In developing the focus of NHS care around the patient, the key areas of change have concentrated upon:

Our vision for primary and community care. July 2008 (GR 10096). Department of Health.

- shaping services around people's needs and views
- promoting healthy lives and tackling health inequalities
- continually improving health
- ensuring that change is led locally

Our vision for primary and community care proposed that the reforms in 2006 to the dental contract were a 'stronger platform' to deliver services but pointed out that access remains a particular concern in some areas and that 'services need to adapt to changing oral health needs'.

¶3.23, p 21.

The NHS spends around £100 billion per year on healthcare in England and a large proportion of that sum is spent, or committed by clinicians in primary care through direct treatment, prescribing or onward referral. The reality is that in most PCTs the primary care dental budget amounts to about 5 per cent of the total PCT spend and about 0.5 to 2 per cent would be the Patient Charge Revenue (PCR) risk. In terms of cost pressure, mental health budgets and commissioning secondary care are allocated a much higher spend and present more of a financial burden than dentistry.

Commissioning dental services

In simple terms the NHS is responsible for providing services that help prevent diseases of the mouth, teeth and gums and provide appropriate care and treatment where disease occurs. The main diseases are caries, periodontal disease and oral cancer.

World class commissioning: improving dental access, quality and oral health. January 2009 (GR 1100). Department of Health.

The ranges of dental services to be commissioned are:

- mandatory services through GDS Providers
- out of hours services
- specialist primary care services such as orthodontics, oral surgery and sedation services which can be provided either as additions to mandatory services or under specialist PDS agreements
- salaried primary dental care services for groups with special needs
- dental access centres.

The driver for much of commissioning since 2006 has been to improve access to NHS dental services. At its peak in 1993, around 60 per cent of the population used NHS dental services within a given two-year period. This figure dropped substantially over the years, particularly after the effects of the fee cut in 1992 and then again after the introduction of the 2006 contract.

The government has given all PCTs projections to meet access targets by 2013.

Commissioning specialist services

PCTs may wish to consider services provided by Dentists with Special Interests (DwSIs) as part of the planning and commissioning of services to meet the health needs of their population in the most cost effective manner without compromising quality. As part of their general commissioning of primary dental services they can commission Advanced Mandatory Services to be provided on referral by any dentist willing to undertake them.

The first clinical competency frameworks to be made available were:

- orthodontics
- dento-alveolar surgery
- periodontics
- endodontics.

These are the areas where PCTs may wish to commission services through General Dental Services (GDS) Contracts or Personal Dental Services (PDS) Agreements for those whose practices are limited to one specialty (such as orthodontics).

Primary Dental Services: Commissioning Specialist Dental Services. Revised version. December 2005 (GR 5865). Department of Health.

In December 2005 the Department of Health issued guidance on how specialist services should be commissioned from April 2006. This focused on orthodontics and oral surgery, but also included what it called 'Specialised Services': Domiciliary Services and Sedation.

In the future PCTs may consider commissioning other specialties such as endodontics, paediatric dentistry, periodontics, prosthodontics and restorative dentistry. Not all these areas will require separate specialist contracts: many will be included as part of the 'mandatory services' provided by GDS and PDS dentists, or may be provided in secondary care.

Many of these services will be commissioned for patients referred to specialists and DwSIs and may come from a wide geographical area, not just within one PCT. In other words, a PCT may be providing services for patients not resident in its area. Different PCTs may therefore come together to co-ordinate and agree specialist commissioning across their Strategic Health Authority area overseen by the local Consultant in Dental Public Health.

It remains to be seen how cost effective commissioning services from DwSIs will be, since practitioners who have gone to the enormous lengths to become accredited in this way are unlikely to offer their services for the equivalent of either current NHS patient charges or old GDS fees. The comparator will be the cost of obtaining the service in secondary care – for example, dento-alveolar surgery – or in the private sector.

Specialist services can be commissioned from dental practices in two ways: as additional services added on to a GDS Contract or PDS Agreement; or as a separate PDS Agreement where the practice only carries out such services (such as a practice limited to orthodontics). In 2005 Primary Care Contracting issued a factsheet on specialist practitioners whose GDS work was limited to orthodontics or other specialist services who had to transfer into a new PDS Agreement in April 2006.

Implementing Local Commissioning for Primary Care Dentistry, Factsheet 3: Making New PDS Agreements for Specialist Services. (GR 5917).

Access, quality and choice

As access targets are met in the coming years, commissioning strategies will increasingly focus on ensuring quality and choice are improved in dental services.

Quality framework or score cards have been developed to draw together all the data from a variety of sources to enable commissioners to identify strength and weaknesses and to target resources at Providers who need support or close management.

Quality will also be monitored by the Care Quality Commission to ensure that practices meet essential requirements for quality, including patient safety.

Improving oral health

In the future commissioners will need to have a stronger focus on reducing inequalities and developing strong partnerships with Providers to deliver this. As a result, they must ensure that evidence-based interventions are widely adopted by all practices. They also have a responsibility to adopt population-based interventions, such as water fluoridation. A recent example of this, in Southampton, has been billed as 'the single biggest factor in reducing inequalities in oral health'.

The Water Act (2003) allows new fluoridation schemes to be developed where there is agreement to do so after widespread local consultation. While fluoridation remains controversial, there is significant literature that supports its use in reducing tooth decay. There is very little evidence of health risks caused by what detractors describe as 'mass medication'. Seventy per cent of the US and over 60 per cent of the Australian population already drink fluoridated water.

Fluoridation – the facts. CDO Update March 2008.

Oral Health Needs Assessment Toolkit for Primary Care Trusts. Primary Care Contracting, March 2006.

Choosing Better Oral Health – an oral health plan for England. November 2005 (GR 4790). Department of Health.

In making decisions about where to place growth funding or to reallocate resources when dentists opt out of the NHS, commissioners must take a rational approach to commissioning dental services. The following factors are based on the priorities in the Department of Health document *Choosing Better Oral Health*:

- **Index of multiple deprivation** (2004)
- **Census data** (2001) indicating child poverty, overcrowding, general health, unemployment

- **Health and lifestyle surveys** identifying risk factors such as smoking, alcohol, drug use and general health
- **Caries rates** in 5, 12 and 14 year olds
- **Dental Practice Advisor reports** identifying areas of good practice and scope for improvement of facilities/procedures
- **Dental Reference reports** to assess record keeping and treatment planning.

One of the most significant problems with the way in which primary care dentists have been remunerated since the inception of the NHS is the lack of incentive to provide a service that truly integrates prevention. Over the years lip service has been paid to it in the GDS, but within a fee-per-item system, where no fee actually exist for 'prevention', little has changed.

There are now real opportunities within the contract to change that, particularly as the system moves to paying dentists for a range of activity rather than just for UDAs. The Department of Health, in their document 'Choosing Better Health', summarises the current position thus:

- **Adult oral health** in England has been and still is steadily improving. Today, more adults keep their teeth for life – although many still suffer from tooth decay. However, the number of adults aged 65 with no teeth is high compared to some of the other EU countries. This presents challenges for dentistry in supporting people with an ageing dentition.
- **Child oral health** has also been improving and far fewer children experience tooth decay than they did 30 years ago. Older children in England now have the best oral health in Europe. However, in spite of this overall improvement, national surveys still highlight inequalities which are strongly associated with social background. There are also variations according to other factors, such as water fluoridation.
- **Periodontal (gum) disease** affects a large proportion of the population, especially in adulthood. It can result in teeth becoming loose and having to be extracted.
- **Oral cancer** incidence is rising, accounting for approximately 800 deaths each year. Survival rates increase dramatically if the disease is diagnosed in its early stages, but low awareness and the painless nature of early oral cancer means people generally only seek treatment when the cancer is more advanced and difficult to treat.

The document goes on to identify the factors causing poor oral health such as diet and nutrition (excessive consumption of sugar causing caries and fizzy drinks causing erosion), poor oral hygiene, lack of exposure to fluoride, tobacco and alcohol (increasing the risk of cancer and impacting on periodontal disease) and injury through contact sports.

Dentists have an important part to play in improving the lives of their patients by adopting evidence-based interventions. The outcomes of their interventions affect other aspects of patients' health and is a recognised part of the common risk approach. This recognises that chronic diseases and conditions such as obesity, heart disease, stroke, cancers, diabetes and oral cancer share a set common risk conditions and factors. For example, a poor quality diet, smoking, inadequate hygiene, excessive alcohol intake and trauma are factors linked to the development of several chronic conditions, including oral diseases.

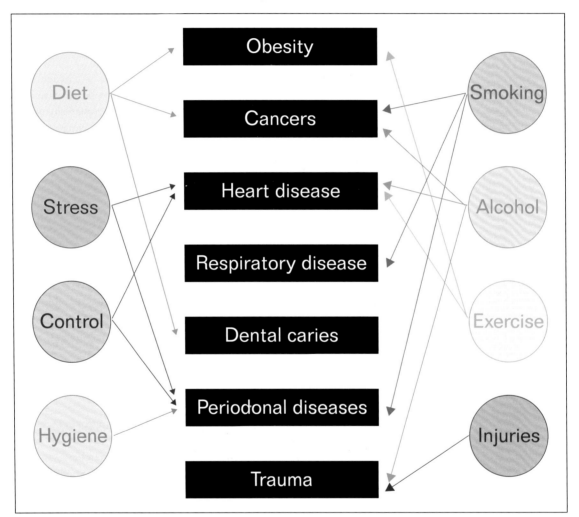

Figure 12: Common risk factors (Taken from *Choosing Better Health*, p23).

The key concept of the integrated common risk approach is that by directing action on these common risks and their underlying social determinants, improvements in a range of chronic conditions will be achieved more efficiently and with greater effectiveness.

Reading your PCT's Public Health Report is very important since it outlines your area's demographic profiles as well as the health inequalities across the PCT boundaries. Considerable focus at present is on the management of chronic disease such as diabetes, heart disease and asthma as well as other priority areas such as mental illness in adults, and adolescent and communicable diseases. What is sometimes quite striking is the considerable variation in the relative wealth and poverty – with their associated health implications – across a very small geographical area.

Implementing oral health into practice

Most dentists regard aspects of prevention as part of their professional work, a source of job satisfaction and of value to the practice, its image and a marker of quality of care. However, the quantity and proportion of working time spent undertaking preventive activity varies widely. The challenge for clinicians is to implement these oral health messages into everyday practice. Many practitioners are already doing so but may not be following a consistent approach or an evidence-based one. Many of these interventions require time, effort and sometimes money: unless clinicians are convinced of their efficacy and are rewarded for their commitments little change will take place.

Fox (2010).

One of the key drivers for behavioural change will be the monitoring of these activities. While the current Government has set itself against targets, performance measurers linked to remuneration will be necessary.

Delivering Better Oral Health – an evidence based toolkit for prevention. 2007 (GR 8504). Department of Health.

All practices were sent a hard copy of the prevention Toolkit in September 2007 and further copies for each NHS dentist was sent in 2009.Copies can be downloaded from the Department of Health website. The guidance is broken down into a number of sections:

1) Principles of toothbrushing for oral health
2) Increasing fluoride availability
3) Healthy eating advice
4) Identifying sugar-free medicines
5) Improving periodontal health
6) Stop smoking guidance
7) Alcohol information
8) Prevention of erosion

Delivering Better Oral Health, p 10.

For example for prevention of caries in children aged from seven years and young adults outlines the advice shown in Table 3 (overleaf) should be given and professional intervention applied.

	Advice	Professional intervention
All children and young adults	• Brush twice daily • Brush last thing at night and on one other occasion • Use fluoridated toothpaste (1,350ppm fluoride or above) • Spit out after brushing and do not rinse • The frequency and amount of sugary food and drinks should be reduced and, when consumed, limited to mealtime. Sugars should not be consumed more than four times per day	• Apply fluoride varnish to teeth twice yearly (2.2%F)
Those giving concern (e.g. those likely to develop caries, those undergoing orthodontic treatment, those with special needs)	All the above plus: • Use a fluoride mouth rinse daily (0.05%NaF) at a different time to brushing • Consider recommending an oscillating or rotating power toothbrush	• Fissure seal permanent molars with resin sealant • Apply fluoride varnish to teeth 3-4 times yearly (2.2%F) • For those 8+ years with active caries prescribe daily fluoride rinse • For those 10+ years with active caries prescribe 2,800ppm toothpaste • For those 16+ years with active disease consider prescription of 5,000ppm toothpaste • Investigate diet and assist adoption of good dietary practices

Table 3: Advice and professional intervention for preventing caries.

It is increasingly likely that practices will be expected to deliver this advice and interventions and that their remuneration will be linked to this.

The clinical data set information collected from NHS claims records the application of fluoride varnish and fissure sealants: commissioners are using this information to establish the preventive focus of practices. Other measures already in use in PDS contracts include:

- percentage of patients attending who have a record of their smoking status
- percentage of identified smokers who have been signposted to smoking cessation services
- percentage of patients requiring toothbrushing advice who have been given toothbrushing advice
- percentage of courses of treatment for child patients requiring fissure sealants where application has been recorded
- percentage of treatment for child patients where fluoride varnish has been recorded.

Introducing these interventions into the practice requires a team approach so that all clinicians are delivering a consistent message. It also means that Dental Care Professionals (DCPs) can deliver the messages to patients once they have been suitably trained.

Smoke free and smiling: helping dental patients to quit tobacco. 2007 (GR 8177). Department of Health. Raja *et al.* (2006).

Clear advice and scripts are available and the evidence for brief dental interventions in changing smoking behaviours is compelling. The same cannot be said for advice about alcohol reduction and studies conclude that GDPs felt that alcohol based discussions in primary care would not be relevant and would inevitably lead to disruption of the patient-clinician relationship.

Barber (2010); Dyer *et al.* (2006).

A key plank in delivering what the government describes as the three dimensions of quality – patient experience, patient safety and clinical effectiveness – is the need for good clinical leadership. This will have to come from consultants in dental public health and similar specialists. There is, however, a significant lack of capacity in the dental public health workforce: an additional 50 whole-time consultant and six whole-time dental practice advisors for England need to be provided.

Improving oral health and dental outcomes: developing the dental public health workforce in England. 2010 (GR 13937). Department of Health.

Procurement and tendering

In order to increase the level of service in an area or change the nature of service provision, such as introducing specialist services, commissioners have to procure dental services. This may happen at any point in the financial year. The need to tender may also arise if an existing Provider leaves the NHS or the commissioner claws back money from underperforming contracts and wishes to reinvest the money in dental services.

Commissioners can either increase services by offering existing Providers more activity – in the form of UDAs tied to certain delivery criteria – or they can enter into tender process. In order to achieve access targets commissioners have developed schemes such as extended hours provision and 'Tiny Teeth' programmes aimed at increasing access for young children.

Primary dental services fall under 'medical services'. As these are on the B list for OJEU (Official Journal of the European Union) they are exempt from many of the obligations under EU Directives including the requirement to publish the contract notice in the OJEU or the full tendering process. Nevertheless, in order to ensure transparency a clear procurement process must be followed. Commissioners must ensure that:

- fair competition is undertaken and that no potential supplier/bidder is disadvantaged by the process or requirements to tender
- the decision to award a contract is based upon evaluation criteria that are linked to the requirements of the specific documentation and that is can be determined
- specifications must include all technical and professional requirements

● an award notice is placed through OJEU.

Although the full tender process does not have to be applied when procuring primary dental services, the principles of fairness and open competition must still be applied, and suppliers who are not successful may make a legal challenge if they believe this was not the case.

Procurement of primary dental service case study: North Cumbria PCTs. Primary Care Contracting.

The concept of 'any willing provider' (AWP) has been developed to ensure that patients have a choice where they receive services. This is particularly the case for elective medical services. Commissioners often advertise in the *British Dental Journal* and from September 2008 it has been mandatory to advertise procurement and contract awards on the NHS website.

www.supply2health.nhs.uk

Where services are not contracted for on an AWP model, tendering can be used to secure a new contract, especially when:

● a current contract expires or is terminated
● a new service model or significant additional capacity is needed.

Procurement guide for commissioners of NHS funded services. July 2010 (GR 14611). Department of Health.

Once the commissioner decides to use procurement, they may choose variations on some of the following tendering approaches:

● single tender action (i.e. uncontested procurement)
● open competition
● restricted competition
● competitive dialogue.

When tendering, commissioners must comply with the Public Contracts Regulations 2006.

Coates (2009).

The tender process varies amongst commissioners. However, it inevitably requires a significant time investment to tender successfully for NHS contracts. Practices run by Corporate bodies are often believed to be at an advantage because they have reduced operating costs and management teams specifically dedicated to win new contracts. Single surgery practices or associates looking to set up on their own often lack the necessary evidence to be competitive in this arena.

Tendering stages

1) Potential bidders are invited to express an interest (EOI). This process allows the commissioners to assess the interest in their tenders.

2) Interested bidders complete a pre-qualification questionnaire (PQQ).

3) The PQQs are scored according to pre-determined criteria and shortlisted Providers are then given full tender documents on-line and invited to submit a tender (invitation to tender – ITT). The bidders are given the full technical specification of the tender at this time in the memorandum of information (MOI), setting out what the commissioners want for the service and how they would

like it operated in general terms. They may indicate the likely costs and value of the tender.

4) Shortlisted Providers from this stage are invited to give a presentation on their proposals and business plan and attend a meeting with the commissioners to respond to questions.

5) The final decision is made and the successful bidder informed. Contract negotiations may still take place with the successful Provider over the specifics of delivering the contract.

The documentation for an ITT can run to several dozen pages, covering not just the cost at which you are willing to provide the service at but other themes such as:

Jones *et al.* (2009).

- business details of the practice including financial information and details of performance on other NHS contracts
- how the potential Provider will ensure provision of access to NHS dental services for residents in the locale
- confirmation of how the potential Provider will provide high quality general dental services that meet the demands of diverse population groups
- how the potential Provider will establish positive working relationships opening times, proportion of NHS commitment, promotion of NHS brand and proposed staffing structure, including recruitment strategies
- contingency arrangements for loss of staffing, major incidents or communications failure, and disaster recovery plans
- indicative prices associated with the delivery of the number of UDAs with the PCT in order to maximise service delivery
- details of the proposed locations.

For practices that wish to expand the NHS services they provide, understanding the procurement process is an essential prerequisite. Being familiar with the information required and having it prepared in the templates that are easily obtainable will ensure that if a tender becomes available you are ready and waiting.

4 THE DENTAL TEAM WORKING TOGETHER

Contractors

The Contractor can be:

- an individual dentist
- two or more dentists acting in partnership
- a dental body corporate (known in the Regulations as a **Dental Corporation**).

Most primary care trusts (PCTs) commission from practices rather than practitioners. A practice may consist of a single dentist, who could be an associate. It is possible for other dentists – associates – working within the practice to hold their own contract and remain personally responsible for the services they provide as they did previously. This however is rare.

In any model the practice goodwill remains in the practice owners' hands. It is necessary to negotiate an associate agreement within a practice. If an associate moves on, the practice can keep the full contract value provided it continues to provide the same level of service. Otherwise it goes back to the PCT. When an associate moves to a new practice, the associate or new practice will need to agree a new contract with their PCT or to amend the current one.

Dental corporates are able to hold a contract with the PCT and must agree contracts with the dentists working within them.

General Dental Service Regulation 4 lays down the conditions that would bar a dentist from being a Contractor. These include:

- disqualification
- dismissal by a health service body
- conviction of a serious crime including such as those against children or young persons
- bankruptcy
- receivership
- some financial misdemeanours.

However Regulations 4(3) and 4(5) allow the PCT some latitude in applying these rules.

Performers

Primary care dentists in GDS, PDS or salaried services must be on the Performers List. Those in vocational training have two months in which to apply to go on a list. Practice owners/contract holders do not need to be Performers if they do no NHS work. It would, however, be prudent for them to be on the PCT's List in case they have to see an associate's NHS patients in an emergency.

® NHS (Performers Lists) Amendment 2005: Statutory Instrument No. 3491. See Part 3, Dental Performers Lists.

Performers Lists are covered by Regulations. These lay down who can be on a List and what information is needed when you apply. They also describe the circumstances under which a PCT can refuse to admit you or can remove someone.

You need only be on the Performers List of one PCT, normally the one in which you work. This also applies if you are working in two or more PCT areas or go to work temporarily in another PCT area. If you are working in a PCT area where you are not on the list, they will need to know on which list you are entered. If you move to another PCT, it is normal to be removed from the old list and to join the new one.

From time to time PCTs will seek to 'clean' their Lists of those who have died, have retired or are not active. They also need to ensure that everyone on their List is still eligible to be there: for example, are they still on the Dentists Register? This might apply if you are a practice owner who normally does no NHS work, or someone taking a career break. But even if you have done no work recently you are still entitled to be on a List if eligible.

Associates

Any associate who had a GDS Contract on 31 March 2006 was entitled to their own new GDS Contract, but most practice owners negotiated a practice-based contract to retain control. This needed some change to the associate's contract, which had to be agreed between the parties; by choosing not to have their own contract the associate was giving up some rights.

Under the old GDS Contract the associate generated income for the practice; under a new practice-based contract the practice income for the year is agreed at the beginning. The associate becomes a spender of that income, in terms of both their own remuneration and any expenses that they may incur, such as laboratory fees. This must be taken into account in any negotiation of their contract.

Their remuneration should take into account the need for them to maintain a required level of activity once the incentive of being paid per item of service is removed. The high-grossing/fast-working associate may be less in demand, especially if they run up large laboratory bills. An associate prepared to carry out simple routine work on NHS patients may be preferred, with a corresponding reduction in their level of earnings.

Given the change of relationship between practice owner and associate brought on by the 2006 contract, there can be some confusion about an associate's status: specifically, whether they are employed or self-employed. HM Revenue and Customs has indicated that it will not interfere with the present position. It would be wise, however, to discuss this matter with your accountant.

▶ Chapter 9, 'Managing associates', p 100.

Vocational dental practitioners

Vocational dental practitioners (VDPs) are now known as foundation dentists to reflect the educational imperative that is the dental foundation year 1 training programme.

The arrangements for dental vocational training were revised under the 2006 contract and are likely to continue for the foreseeable future. The most significant change was to the funding arrangements with approved Trainers receiving gross funding in the region of £100,000: this is to include the Trainer's Grant, reimbursement of the trainee's salary and a further payment to cover fixed and variable costs associated with having a trainee in practice. These are collectively known as service costs.

Trainers, who are approved for their post by the office of the Postgraduate Dental Dean, receive this funding via the payments on line (POL) system via the PCT in 12 equal monthly instalments. The trainees are required to work in practice under a nationally agreed contract of employment. They are Performers and work under GDS Regulations but their activity is outside the contracted activity of the training practice. Though not a target, trainees are allocated a notional activity level of 1,875 UDAs. It is emphasised that this is not a target and as such there is no penalty for under-performance as there may be under GDS (if the 4 per cent tolerance is exceeded). There is also no extra remuneration for over-activity.

At the end of the training year, the trainee may wish to continue to work at the practice. However, funding for their continuation must come from existing practice contract value or from growth monies allocated by the PCT. There is no automatic guarantee for this.

Dentists with Special Interests

Dentists with Special Interests (DwSIs) provide services which are complementary to secondary care, but they do not replace those dentists who have undergone the training required for entry to the specialist lists. They are independent practitioners who work within the limits of their competency in providing a special interest service but who refer on where necessary.

DwSIs may deliver a clinical service beyond that normally provided by a primary dental care practitioner or may deliver a particular type of treatment. They must be able to demonstrate their competencies in special interest areas. PCTs are able to contract with DwSIs to provide enhanced services with improved access to meet the identified needs of the local population. It is not known how many PCTs take advantage of these skills, although in general medical practice GPs with special interests are quite extensively used.

The concept of a DwSI is not new. The intention of the new scheme is to move towards supporting the accreditation of DwSIs within a quality assurance framework which can be relied on by PCTs and the patients using their services. The scheme focuses primarily on DwSIs delivering clinical services and PCTs will consider whether these skills are required. They will have an obligation to make sure that those who need 'advanced mandatory services' are seen and treated.

Implementing a Scheme for Dentists with Special Interests (DwSIs). DH / FGDP(UK) GR 2788 (May 2004).

In 2004 the Department of Health and Faculty of General Dental Practitioners (UK) published a paper on DwSIs. These were defined as any dentist working in primary care who provides services which are in addition to their usual generalist role. The paper described them as complementary to secondary services as a whole, but not to replace those dentists who are on a specialist list.

Dentists with Special Interests (DwSIs), A step by step guide to setting up a DwSI service. April 2006. NHS Primary Care Contracting.

In April 2006 the NHS published guidance on setting up a Dentist with a Special Interest service, together with specific guidance on endodontics, orthodontics, periodontics and minor oral surgery. This was followed by the launch of competency frameworks in prison dentistry in November 2007 and conscious sedation in January 2008. In April 2008, the FGDP(UK) also published its own guidance for competencies and standards in both research and leadership and management.

The DH/FGDP(UK) guidelines for appointing DwSIs can be found in GR 5338 (Endodontics), GR 5340 (Orthodontics), GR 5341 (Periodontics) and GR 5339 (Minor Oral Surgery).

Each of the specialist guidance pubications deals with why DwSIs in the specific specialty are needed, the appropriate competency framework and what evidence is needed to ensure that the DwSI maintains this, and how DwSIs are accredited and appointed.

The main guidance deals with developing these services in primary dental care and the five steps needed to achieve this:

- reviewing the current services
- what the PCT will need
- designing the service
- clinical governance
- audit and evaluation.

More useful information can be found
on the GDC's website
(www.gdc-uk.org).

The other titles that can only be used by
those on the Dentists Register are 'dental
surgeon' and 'dental practitioner'.

Dentists and the GDC

Where Performers and associates are new dentists, they will need to register with the General Dental Council (GDC). The GDC is the regulatory body for dentists working in the UK. Only dentists who are registered with them and appear on the Dentists Register can use the title of 'dentist' and practise dentistry. Anyone with a recognised dental qualification from a university in the European Economic Area (EEA) can apply to be included in the Dentists Register. The EEA consists of the UK and all other EU countries, plus Norway, Iceland and Lichtenstein: those outside the EEA can apply to join the Register, but will have to provide additional evidence of their competence.

Dentists can register any specialist qualifications they have on the Specialist Register. The General Dental Council also maintains a register of Dental Care Professionals (DCPs).

Regulation by GDC

As well as maintaining its Registers, the GDC's functions are to protect patients and regulate the dental team. It fulfils these functions by issuing guidance on issues such as 'scope of practice' for each class of registrant and by supervising the work of the Dental Complaints Service for non-NHS related complaints. Most significant, from the dentist's point of view, are its 'Fitness to Practise' panels, which can investigate dental professionals. Following its hearings dentists can be erased from the Register and have conditions imposed on their registration.

The important point for any new registrant to grasp is that you are personally responsible for your actions and accountable for them to the GDC. This overrides any obligations you have to the practice where you work or, for example, to your local PCT.

Obligations

In addition to your obligation to act always in the best interests of patients, the GDC lays down specific additional requirements. These include:

Dentists have to renew their registration
annually for the forthcoming calendar
year (1 January – 31 December). DCP
registrants' year runs from 1 July to
30 June.

- You must pay the Annual Retention Fee before 1 January each year.
- You must have your own professional indemnity. (Most dentists are members of one of the main indemnity Providers: Dental Protection, Dental Defence Union, Medical and Dental Defence Union of Scotland.)
- You must carry out 250 hours of Continuing Professional Development over a five year cycle.

Postgraduate education

Continuing Professional Development (CPD) is the first requirement for dentists. It is a compulsory part of registration: if you do not comply you will be removed from the Register. This means you will not be able to work as a dentist anywhere in the UK. The GDC sets the rules, but does not approve or accredit CPD activities. You must complete, and keep records of, at least 250 hours of CPD over five years. A minimum of 75 of these hours must consist of verifiable CPD. Every year the GDC will write to you and ask you to tell them how many hours of verifiable and general CPD you have completed. At the end of your five year cycle they will write again and ask you for the final verifiable and general total for your five year cycle.

Verifiable CPD is that which meets all of the GDC's educational criteria and where your participation can be verified by an appropriate third party. The educational criteria are:

1) the activity must have concise educational aims and objectives
2) the activity must have clear anticipated outcomes
3) there must be an opportunity for you to give feedback on what you think of it.

It is your responsibility to check with the course Provider that the activity meets the educational criteria and to get a certificate. If you fail to do so, you will not be able to count the activity as verifiable.

The GDC also recommends that all dentists carry out CPD in recommended core subjects and that you do CPD in medical emergencies every year. The recommended core subjects and suggested minimum number of verifiable hours per CPD cycle that dentists should spend on them are:

- medical emergencies (at least 10 hours per CPD cycle)
- disinfection and decontamination (at least 5 hours per CPD cycle)
- radiography and radiation protection (at least 5 hours per CPD cycle)

Nowadays there is a wide range of organisations and journals offering CPD. For those who wish to increase their knowledge or obtain an additional qualification there are many courses arranged by postgraduate educational establishments.

The GDC website contains useful Frequently Asked Questions: www.gdc-uk.org/Current + registrant/ CPD + requirements/Frequently + asked + questions + about + CPD/ Dentists + CPD + FAQs.htm

Dental care professionals

The Government believes that the new arrangements, combined with GDC registration of dental care professionals, will allow practices to allocate work across the whole dental team, including hygienists, therapists and oral health educators.

Scope of Practice Guidance.
General Dental Council.

Their scope of practice is outlined in GDC guidance, which sets out the skills and abilities that each member of the team should have. It is not a list of tasks that someone can do. It also describes additional skills that they might develop after registration to increase the scope of their practice. Lastly, the guidance lists 'reserved duties' which they can only practise if they are registered in a particular group. If they want to carry out these duties, they will need to receive further training and gain a qualification which would allow them to register in a different group.

The following members of the dental team need to be registered and maintain their registration, including a commitment to perform continuing professional development:

- dental nurses
- orthodontic therapists
- dental hygienists
- dental therapists
- dental technicians
- clinical dental technicians.

It is the practice owners' responsibility to ensure that their staff are registered: they are liable to disciplinary action if they work with unregistered people.

Obligations of DCPs

As with dentists, the GDC imposes obligations on Dental Care Professionals. These include:

- You must pay the Annual Retention Fee before 1 July each year.
- You must have your own professional indemnity. (Some practices will arrange this for you.)
- You must also carry out 250 hours of Continuing Professional Development over a five-year cycle.

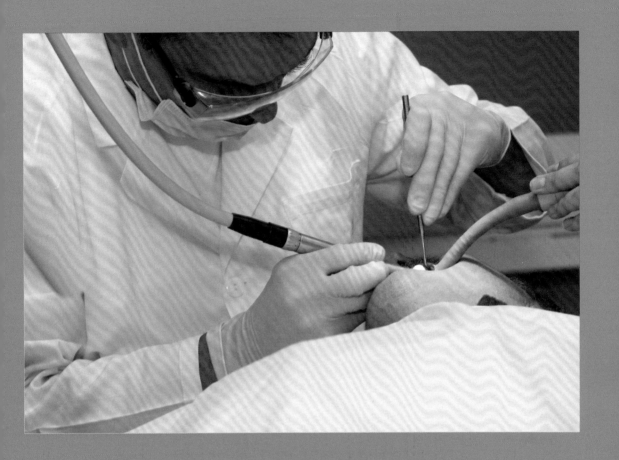

Part Two

WORKING WITH THE CONTRACT

5 CONTRACTING MODELS

The new types of contract

Since 1 April 2006, there have been only two types of contract, although their terms are similar: **General Dental Services Contracts** and **Personal Dental Services Agreements**. Regulations for both were published in August 2005 and laid before Parliament on 9 December. They came into force on 1 January 2006. They set out the terms for GDS Contracts and PDS Agreements, which are binding both on PCTs and dentists. These regulations remain the basis of all contracts now in force.

- **GDS Contracts**

  Under a GDS Contract, the dentist is required to provide a range of dental services known as 'mandatory services', which includes referring complex cases if appropriate. This is what defines a GDS Contract: unless the full range of mandatory services is provided, the dentist cannot hold one. However, a GDS Contract can also include other 'additional services' such as sedation and orthodontics. Most GDS Contracts are not time limited, although some PCTs are asking dentists to agree that they should be limited to a certain number of years.

- **PDS Agreements**

  Practices which do not provide the full range of mandatory services, for example those limited to orthodontics, work under a PDS Agreement. These agreements are also available to those which had previously had a pilot PDS Agreement or were demonstration sites. Those which had a pilot PDS Agreement prior to 31 March 2006 can, however, convert to a GDS Contract. There may be other circumstances in which a PCT may choose to offer a PDS Agreement, rather than a GDS Contract.

These sites were set up following the *Options for Change* report in 2002 to pilot new ways of working.

Contracts and Agreements

Many orthodontic contracts were for an initial period of five years, so this time limit did not apply.

In April 2009 the guarantee of a contract ended and many PDS Agreements, which were limited to three years, needed to be renegotiated or converted to GDS Contracts. GDS Contracts, on the other hand, generally have no time limit and continue. In either case, however, the PCT may seek to vary a contract. In September 2008 NHS Primary Care Contracting (PCC) published guidance on 'major contract reviews', which applies to many contracts after April 2009, when the transitional income guarantee for GDS dentists ends. The briefing does warn, however, that

> there is no compulsion for PCTs to review/re-negotiate all dental contracts as a result of this. It is important that reviews are not driven by an arbitrary date but by a logical local process within a strategic framework. A rolling cycle of reviews with Providers should be established which clearly distinguishes between contract reviews and normal performance reviews.
>
> NHS Dental Contract Reviews Briefing Web/BM/150908 published by NHS PCC, September 2008

The briefing paper sets out a framework that PCTs can use or adapt locally to develop their approach and policy for undertaking major reviews of NHS dentistry contracts. It states that a PCT cannot, within the regulatory framework, impose contract variations unilaterally:

> Where the PCT considers there needs to be a variation to the number of UDAs or UOAs it must notify the Contractor in writing of its proposal together with its reasons for the proposed variation. Both parties must use their best endeavours to reach agreement including any related variation of the contract value.

If the two parties cannot reach agreement, either can ask the NHS Litigation Authority to determine the dispute on the merits of the individual case. The briefing advocates that

◗ Chapter 13, 'Disputes, sanctions and appeals', p 158.

> the process should be open and transparent for all stakeholders; it should be underpinned by the principle of 'no surprises'.

Most contracts between PCTs and practices have been based on the standard GDS Contract, though many PCTs added their own variations, sometimes, but not always, based on the GDS Regulations. Some of these clauses were clinically very prescriptive, such as requiring dentists to apply fluoride varnish twice yearly to the molars of high caries risk children. Some PCTs were adopting measures that were applicable in old PDS to new GDS Contracting arrangements, such as using patients' 'registrations' or numbers of sessions or hours worked as a requirement. Some PCTs have included clauses that would suggest they wish to micromanage the practices, with stipulations about when a Performer can leave and who can replace them, the ratio of banded treatments allowed and the ratio of children and exempts to adults in a practice profile.

More recently PCTs have been seeking to insert clauses into new GDS Contracts limiting their duration. This would apply when a practice is sold and a new owner takes over. Many PCTs do not realise the extent of financial outlay involved in setting up a new practice or buying into an existing one. A dentist needs to cover any borrowings and make a return on the capital investment involved.

PDS Agreements are negotiated locally and can be more flexible, although they must conform to the PDS Regulations and there is a template PDS Agreement to assist PCTs to reach agreement. All PDS Agreements are fixed-term; the duration can be extended by agreement of the parties.

General Dental Services Contract

The new GDS Contract (often referred to as nGDS) is the workhorse of the new system. All GDS Contracts must comply with the requirements of the relevant Act and will need to conform with:

The National Health Service Act 1977, as amended by the Health and Social Care (Community Health and Standards) Act 2003.

Ⓡ NHS (Dental Charges) 2006.

- Directions issued under Section 192 of the Act
- Regulations issued under Section 192 of the Act
- Regulations relating to patients' charges under Section 183 of the Act
- Policy guidance and performance targets issued from time to time by the Department of Health and the Welsh Assembly Government.

Directions

Section 28N.

The Act allows the Secretary of State for Health to give Directions about payments, which must be made under GDS Contracts. These Directions are contained in the Statement of Financial Entitlements, which lays down what PCTs must pay dentists under a GDS Contract. It is normally revised annually.

A consolidated version of the GDS Statement of Financial Entitlements was last published on 9 May 2008 to reflect the rise in contract values recommended by the Doctors' and Dentists' Review Body. It is divided into three parts:

- **Part 1:** Annual Contract Values
  - Calculated Annual Contract Values
  - Negotiated Annual Contract Values
  - Payment of Monthly Annual Contract Value Payments
  - Superannuation contributions

- **Part 2:** Payments for Specific Purposes
  - Domiciliary services and sedation services
  - Seniority payments
  - Payments in respect of vocational training
  - Payments in respect of maternity, paternity and adoption leave
  - Payments in respect of long-term sickness leave
  - Reimbursement of non-domestic rates

● **Part 3:** Administrative Provisions

- Payment arrangements
- Overpayments and withheld amounts
- Underpayments and late payments
- Payments on account
- Time limitation for claiming payments
- Payments to or in respect of suspended dentists whose suspension ceases
- Effect on periodic payments of termination of a GDS Contract
- Recovery of charges relating to work done under pilot schemes
- Payments in and for April 2006
- Dispute resolution procedures

Regulations

The National Health Service (General Dental Services Contracts) Regulations 2006 (GR 5123) and *The National Health Service (Personal Dental Services Agreements) Regulations 2006* (GR 5124).

PCTs are not totally free to agree contracts with their dentists, but are governed by regulations approved by Parliament covering GDS Contracts and PDS Agreements. These regulations are permanent unless amendments are approved by Parliament. However, from time to time PCTs can vary the contractual terms with a practice, subject to agreement with the Contractor.

Part 5 of the GDS Regulations lays down what must be included in a GDS Contract:

- the names of the parties to the contract
- whether or not it is an NHS contract
- the details of any partnership in the practice
- the duration of the contract (this will normally be continuous)
- mandatory services, which every Contractor must provide if the patient needs them, including urgent treatment and the hours when services should be provided
- additional services such as advanced mandatory services, dental public health services, domiciliary services and sedation services
- the address where services are to be provided and the hours during which non-mandatory services are to be provided
- the number of UDAs and units of orthodontic activity (UOAs), as well as action to be taken if there is an under-provision of these units
- a term obliging the PCT to pay the dentist and the circumstances under which they are allowed to withhold payment
- fees, charges and financial interests of the Contractor, what charges a dentist can make to the patient, including statutory patients' charges
- how a contract is terminated.

Patients' charges

Harry Cayton, the National Director for Patients and the Public, chaired a committee on the remodelling of dental patients' charges, which reported to Ministers in March 2004. The committee contained representatives of the profession, dental technicians and consumer groups. Consultation on draft regulations for patients' charges, in both GDS and PDS, took place between July and September 2005. Having been approved by Parliament, the Regulations also took effect on 1 April 2006. The scheme, based on recommendations of the Cayton Report, is a banded system. The patient will pay a single charge appropriate to the highest band in which their treatment occurs.

- **Band 1** – clinical examination, radiographs, scaling and polishing, preventive dental work, such as oral health advice.
- **Band 2** – simple treatment, for example fillings, including root canal therapy, extractions, surgical procedures and denture additions.
- **Band 3** – complex treatment, which includes a laboratory element, such as bridgework, crowns, and dentures.
- **Band 4** – urgent treatment covering examination, radiographs, dressings, recementing crowns, up to two extractions, one filling.

Policy guidance

12 October 2005 (GR 5641). Department of Health.

Factsheet 14, *Salaried Primary Dental Care Services* (DH GR 5917); Factsheet 7, *Commissioning Out-of-Hours Services* (DH GR 5917).

Go to www.pcc.nhs.uk/89.php or CDO's webpage on www.dh.gov.uk.

Policy guidance is issued from time to time by the Department of Health and specific guidance has been given to PCTs. The Department also issues performance frameworks for dentistry, which will give PCTs their targets for the coming years. Guidance has also been given on salaried services, out-of-hours care and the deployment of Dentists with Special Interests (specialists in general practice). PCTs are expected to follow this guidance and are monitored by strategic health authorities. Such guidance is normally published on the Primary Care Contracting website.

Personal Dental Services Agreement

The pilot agreements were set up under the terms of the 1997 Primary Care Act which allowed both Personal Medical Services and PDS to be established as pilot schemes. Their characteristic was that they allowed for new ways of working and remuneration, subject only to approval by the Department of Health.

The original schemes were established as a first wave in 1998 and covered three main areas:

- general dental practice
- community dental service and the establishment of dental access centres
- specialist practice – orthodontics, sedation.

Personal Dental Services (PDS) Pilots: Final Report of the National Evaluation. University of Birmingham School of Dentistry and Health Services Management Centre.

Modernising Dentistry Programme. NHS Modernisation Agency.

There were three subsequent waves in the following years. The working of the first two waves was analysed by a team from the University of Birmingham and the results were, on the whole, positive.

Following the *Options for Change* report, demonstration sites were set up under PDS arrangements. Demonstration sites have also been used where dentists and PCTs have wanted to pilot new ways of working prior to implementation of the 2003 Act.

From April 2006, PDS became permanent, with no more pilots. PDS is confined to the following situations:

- pre-existing PDS contracts where the dentist(s) did not wish to transfer to a new GDS Contract
- where the full range of mandatory services are not going to be provided – for example, practices limited to orthodontics
- where a PCT wants dentists to work outside the confines of the GDS Contract, for instance by adopting a different method of remuneration or different calculation of output.

PDS Regulation 12 lays down that a PDS Agreement must stipulate both the services to be provided and those to whom the services are to be provided. This could allow a PCT and dentist to agree that a certain group of patients will be seen, e.g. children or older people, or that only certain treatments are to be provided, which could apply to Dentists with Special Interests.

As with a GDS Contract, a PDS Agreement has certain required terms, which are laid down in Part 5 of the PDS Regulations:

- whether it is to be an NHS contract
- whether 'additional services' are to be provided
- what services are to be provided and to whom, the duration of the agreement, the practice address
- the required number of UDAs and/or UOAs
- what happens in the case of under-provision of UDAs or UOAs
- any domiciliary and/or sedation services to be provided
- a term obliging the PCT to pay the dentist and the circumstances under which they are allowed to withhold payment
- fees, charges and financial interests of the Contractor, what charges a dentist can make to the patient, including statutory patients' charges
- how a contract is terminated.

R 21 P6.

A dentist who is providing the full range of services under a PDS Agreement has a right to a GDS Contract at any time, subject to giving due notice to the PCT in accordance with the Regulations. Notice must be given to the PCT and, provided certain basic conditions are met, the dentist can transfer.

The regulations allow for a smooth transfer from one scheme to the other, with conditions as to the number of UDAs and finance being the same in both contracts. Unless agreed otherwise, the new GDS Contract must be for the same activity and services. The Regulations do not specifically state the new contract must be for the same financial value; however this is probably implicit. Likewise, it is implicit that the new GDS Contract should be without term.

PDS Plus

In 2009 a new contract framework was devised by the Dental Access Team at the Department of Health, called the 'Personal Dental Services Plus Agreement'. This controversial version of the contract was described by the BDA as 'unnecessarily complex'. It runs to nearly 50 pages and has 17 schedules.

The CDO for England described it as follows:

> To ensure we improve people's access to NHS dentistry, we have developed a template agreement that PCTs can use to commission new services. The agreement will allow PCTs to count the number of new patients as well as the amount of work that dentists do, and enable them to reward dentists for the quality of the services they provide.

The essential changes lie in the method of calculating the annual agreement value, which consists of payments for the following:

- units of dental activity (about 50 per cent of the agreement value)
- number of patients seen within previous 24 months (about 20 per cent)
- the achievement of certain Key Performance Indicators (about 30 per cent).

Such contracts and agreements are called 'blended contracts' and appear to represent the future.

Contractual changes

NHS Primary Care Dentistry: PCT powers in relation to contractual changes, NHS Primary Care Contracting, May 2008.

Guidance issued in May 2008 outlined the powers that PCTs have in relation to changes to contracts and contractual status. The types of changes included:

- retirement
- 24-hour retirement
- death of a practitioner
- sale of a practice
- change of ownership
- change from sole practitioner to partnership
- dissolution or termination of a partnership

- incorporation
- change from a PDS Agreement to a GDS Contract.

The guidance stresses that dental contracts and agreements are personal and therefore not assignable. Although Contractors have every right to sell their practices they have no right to pass on the NHS contract. Likewise a PCT has no obligation 'whatsoever' to any prospective purchaser that the seller may have found. Where a practice is being sold, it is for the PCT to decide whether or not to offer a new contract or agreement, and on what terms – or to test the market. PCTs are reminded that although it is unlawful to buy or sell the goodwill of a GP practice, no such restriction applies to the goodwill of a dental practice. However, any financial arrangement when a dental practice is sold – including the goodwill associated with that business – is a matter between the purchaser and the seller: the PCT should not be involved.

The last Government's response to the Health Committee argued, on the other hand, that these restrictions on the sale of practices do not prevent their having

> what may well be an enhanced goodwill value, so long as the practice is offering services that are valued by the PCT and local patients.

CM 7470 (October 2008).

It advised that the 'key is for the practice to discuss with the PCT any proposed sale early in the process'.

When considering what type of new contract to offer, PCTs have been advised to consider whether a time limited GDS Contract would be appropriate. According to the guidance:

> Compared to a PDS Agreement with a similar term, this might give the PCT added flexibility as the Contractor would have no right to an open ended GDS Contract.

6 PATIENTS

Who will you see?

The NHS in England: the Operating Framework for 2008/09, Department of Health December 2007 ¶2.35.

Government response to Health Select Committee report: October 2008, ¶37.

There is now no registration, thus no list of registered NHS patients that you are obliged to see. Your PCT, however, is required to ensure 'year-on-year improvements in the number of patients accessing NHS dental services' in the previous two years. In addition, the previous Government recognised the significance still attached to the term 'registration', and promised to look at whether some form of registration could be introduced. The Steele Review recommended the re-introduction of registration to ensure continuing care for those patients who want it.

Adult Dental Health Survey, 1998. Section 6.3.2, p 258.

Most patients (86 per cent) attend a practice that they have visited before, with three in five reporting that they had attended the same practice for five years or more. These are your practice patients: some seen under the NHS, some privately and some under both NHS and private arrangements.

A patient is defined in the Regulations as:

> **a person to whom the Contractor is providing services under the contract.**

An important aspect of this statutory definition is that it applies only to the present: '*is*', not 'was' or 'will be'. In other words, when you are not treating the patient they become, for all intents and purposes, a member of the public, rather than a patient of your practice. Once a course of treatment is completed, your obligations under the NHS also end, but they remain a patient of your practice. In most cases they will expect to return there and you will expect to see them again either under the NHS or privately.

You may be urged by your PCT to recall your patients at an appropriate interval, in accordance with the NICE guidelines. There is nothing in the Regulations that obliges you to see patients who have attended previously unless your contract with the PCT has stipulated this: in that case you have a defined list of patients to whom you are contractually obliged to provide services under the NHS.

Unless stipulated otherwise in your contract, you may see patients from outside your PCT area.

Discrimination

According to the Regulations, the Contractor

> shall only refuse to provide services under this Contract to a person if it has reasonable grounds for doing so which do not relate to a person's race, gender, social class, age, religion, sexual orientation, appearance, disability, medical or dental condition; or a person's decision or intended decision to accept private services in respect of himself or his family.

Ⓡ S3 ¶1(3).

It is a breach of your contractual terms to assess a patient on the NHS, privately or for free, and then to refuse to treat them on the NHS purely on the basis of the fact that they require a lot of dental treatment.

❧ 'Capacity planning', p 60.

If you are up to your full capacity you could provide pain relief and then:

- put them on your NHS waiting list and agree to see them at a later date when you have more capacity
- contact the PCT and agree further funding and units of dental activity (UDAs) for this patient and other patients if you find that an increased number of new patients are attending who require large courses of treatment
- refer them to a colleague who does have capacity or growth funding, either in your practice or in the PCT locality.

You must also inform patients of their right to express a preference to receive services from a particular dentist and to make a record of any preference they have. You must endeavour to comply with any reasonable preference expressed by them, but this may not always be possible.

Ⓡ S3 ¶2.

Withdrawal from treatment

Where a patient has committed an act of violence against the dentist or a member of the practice staff or anyone on the practice premises, and the matter has been reported to the police, the dentist can tell the PCT that the practice will no longer provide services to that patient. The PCT is then responsible for telling the patient. Where a patient refuses to pay NHS charges before or during treatment, the dentist may also refuse to begin the course of treatment or withdraw from the case before its completion. You can withdraw from treatment if in your reasonable opinion there is an 'irrevocable breakdown in the relationship':

> Where, in the reasonable opinion of the Contractor, there has been an irrevocable breakdown in the relationship between patient and that Contractor, and notice of such a breakdown has been given to the patient by the Contractor, the Contractor may notify the PCT

Ⓡ S3 ¶5.

that it will no longer provide services to that patient under the contract.

You may not make a charge for failed appointments. Many PCTs, however, have an agreed policy on a specific number of failed-to-attends (e.g. two fail-to-attends in a row) which then allows you to decline further treatment. A policy agreed with the PCT will ensure that any patient complaints about your actions with regards to failed appointments will be supported by the PCT.

It may be worth remembering that you are only obliged to carry out treatment that the patient is willing to undergo. Some patients will want 'everything done'; others will just want an extraction, say, or a filling replaced. If you find out what the patient wants, it may reduce the number of patients who fail to attend.

Regular care

Ten years ago Professor Murray considered the relationship of dental attendance and oral disease and suggested that dentists

> **should try to persuade people to maintain contact with their dentist, even if it is irregularly, and that the visit should be 'asymptomatic' rather than driven by pain.**

Murray (1996).

The Department of Health is committed to the concept of regular care. In its *Framework Proposals* it stresses the importance of continuity of care for 'your' patients, but also emphasises that those needing urgent care should be able to have access to services:

Framework proposals for primary dental services in England from 2005. DH, March 2004.

> Patients should be encouraged to enter into a continuing relationship with their dentist but those not wishing to do so should be offered such care and treatment as is appropriate considering their overall oral health and which they are willing to undergo.
>
> PCTs may wish to vary the contract for dentists to provide care for an agreed group of patients or section of the community. Groups identified could include people from an area of social deprivation or from an area where it is particularly difficult to access care. Equally dentists may wish to vary their patient profiles and improve their practices. But this varying of the contract can only be done through mutual agreement. The provision of additional NHS commitment would attract additional payment.

Authors' note: They could do this by offering a PDS Agreement for specified patients rather than a GDS Contract for all patients.

NHS dental services in England: An independent review led by Professor Jimmy Steele (June 2009).

Professor Steele in his review stressed the importance of continuity of care and building a relationship between dentist and patient over a lifetime. He did acknowledge that not everyone wanted such a commitment:

> Continuity of care matters to patients and to dentists. It is important in building a relationship of trust and a philosophy of lifelong care. This is at the heart of the pathway, but a continuing care relationship

implies responsibilities and rights on both sides. We recommend that patients registered in a continuing care relationship with a practice have an absolute right to return to that practice for both routine and urgent care.

Not everyone wants to have a continuing care relationship with a dentist and it is important that their needs are met too. Provision of urgent care is a fundamental responsibility for the NHS and for PCT commissioners and we recommend that urgent care services should be accessible and commissioned to a high and consistent level of quality.

Urgent treatment

Adult Dental Health Survey, 1998: Section 6.1, p 229.

 P1(2).

According to the 1998 Adult Dental Health Survey, 30 per cent of dentate adults said that they attended only when they had trouble with their teeth. Most of these were unregistered under the old system and some will have received 'occasional treatment'. Since April 2006, they can be seen under the 'urgent treatment' rules:

> Urgent treatment means a course of treatment that consists of one or more of the treatments listed in Schedule 4 to the NHS Charges Regulations (urgent treatment under Band 1 charge) that are provided to a person in circumstances where:
> - a prompt course of treatment is provided because, in the opinion of the Contractor, that person's oral health is likely to deteriorate significantly, or the person is in severe pain by reason of his oral condition; and
> - treatment is provided only to the extent that is necessary to prevent that significant deterioration or address that severe pain.

You can agree with your PCT to see such patients at designated times during the week. Although you are not obliged to participate in this way of working, PCTs are under pressure to ensure that anyone needing urgent treatment receives it. They may therefore want you to have so-called 'open access sessions' written into your contract.

It is important for your receptionist to make clear to the patient whether or not they are being seen on an 'urgent' basis and for you to keep adequate notes so that you can justify your actions. It is also important that all dentists understand the 'urgent treatment' rules. When claiming for urgent treatment the records should reflect the clinical situation – that is, the history and severity of the pain – the diagnosis and the action taken to manage it. However, if the patient is not in pain, but something – for example, a broken filling – is found at a routine examination, then this is not 'urgent treatment'.

Capacity planning

Capacity is the upper limit or ceiling of UDA activity that a practice can operate at. There are three aspects to capacity planning.

1) **Design capacity:** This refers to the maximum output that can possibly be achieved in your practice taking into account the treatment rooms available and operating hours. In other words, it is the upper limit of what your practice is able and designed to deliver.

2) **Effective capacity:** Effective capacity is the maximum possible output given the constraints of the real world which include availability of the dental team to work outside normal hours.

3) **Actual output:** This is usually less than the effective capacity because of lost time through failed appointments, absence, equipment malfunction and other events that conspire to reduce output.

Every practice has its regular patients, both NHS and private. You should set aside specific times in your appointment book to see your 'regular' patients. If, for instance, you recommend that a patient returns in one year's time, you need to make sure that you have the capacity to see them. In effect they are booking an appointment twelve months later and to that extent they have priority over new patients. We call this **reserved capacity**; it is allocated as a result of the commitment entered into at the time of the clinical risk assessment and recall interval recommendation after a course of treatment has been completed.

If your appointment book's designated NHS slots are full, then your practice is up to capacity and you will not be taking on new patients. This is a judgement for you to make, as is the question of how far ahead you should book. Some dentists book the patient in for their next examination when they complete a course of treatment; others operate a recall system. This again is your choice. As you have to finish a course of treatment within a reasonable time, it is likely that you will only take on patients if you are able to complete their treatment within a short period of time. It is by considering factors such as this that you will decide whether you have the capacity to take on new patients.

There is a further aspect to capacity that must be considered. In a busy practice, the inter-appointment waiting time may be, say, four weeks. How should this practice best manage a patient who requires four consecutive appointments? If each successive appointment is booked at the conclusion of a previous one, then 12 weeks will elapse from the time of the examination to the time of completion of treatment. This may go against the contractual requirement to complete courses of treatment in a 'reasonable' period of time, but it will also lead to misleading activity data in the early months of a new contracting year because activity will only be recorded at the conclusion of a course of treatment. For Performers who are paid on completed UDAs, it may also result in poor cash flow. In this situation, the practice may wish to keep open treatment slots in the appointment book so that those four appointments may be accommodated within say a two-week period. This advance allocation of treatment slots we call **allocated capacity**.

Your appointment book

Effective management of your appointment book is key to working with the 2006 contract, whether you are in mixed practice or predominately NHS practice. Your contract will allow for the allocation of time to carry out specialist services and/or 'open access sessions' for the care of those needing urgent treatment. You will need to allocate times when you will see NHS and private patients. You should also consider how many patients you can accept for treatment each month and, especially, how many of them need laboratory work. This must be considered in conjunction with the monitoring system. It is important to ensure that treatment that is started is completed as soon as possible to enable you to claim your UDAs. This means that priority slots should be left every week in the appointment book for treatment to be completed. Alternatively, it may be preferable to pre-book a number of treatment slots for a particular patient who has to make a number of visits.

Patients' Charges

◗ page 52 above.

Consultation on draft regulations for patients' charges, in both GDS and PDS, took place between July and September 2005. Having been approved by Parliament, the Regulations also took effect on 1 April 2006. The scheme, based on recommendations of the Cayton Report, is a banded system. The patient pays a single charge appropriate to the highest band in which their treatment occurs.

Band 1 (1 UDA)

Clinical examination, radiographs, scaling and polishing, preventive dental work, such as oral health advice.

    a) Clinical examination, case assessment and report

    b) Orthodontic case assessment and report

    c) Advice, dental charting, diagnosis and treatment planning

    d) Radiographic examination including panoral and lateral headplates, and radiological report

    e) Study casts including in association with occlusal analysis

    f) Colour photographs

    g) Instruction in the prevention of dental and oral disease including dietary advice and dental hygiene instruction

    h) Surface application as primary preventive measures of sealants and topical fluoride preparations

i) Scaling, polishing and marginal correction of fillings

j) Taking material for pathological examination

k) Adjustments to and easing of dentures or orthodontic appliances

l) Treatment of sensitive cementum

Band 1 – Urgent treatment (1.2 UDAs)

Treatment including examination, radiographs, dressings, recementing crowns, up to two extractions, one filling.

a) Examination, assessment and advice

b) Radiographic examination and radiological report

c) Dressing of teeth and palliative treatment

d) Pulpectomy or vital pulpotomy

e) Re-implantation of a luxated or subluxated permanent tooth following trauma including any necessary endodontic treatment

f) Repair and refixing of inlays and crowns

g) Refixing a bridge

h) Temporary bridges

i) Extraction of not more than two teeth

j) Provision of postoperative care including treatment of infected sockets

k) Adjustment and alteration of dentures or orthodontic appliances

l) Urgent treatment for acute conditions of the gingivae or oral mucosa, including treatment for pericorinitis or for ulcers and herpetic lesions and any necessary oral hygiene instruction in connection with such treatment

m) Treatment of sensitive cementum or dentine

n) Incising an abscess

o) Other treatment immediately necessary as a result of trauma

p) Not more than one permanent filling in amalgam, composite resin, synthetic resin, glass ionomer, compomers, silicate or silico-phosphate including acid etch retention

Band 2 (3 UDAs)

Simple treatment, for example fillings, including root canal therapy, extractions, surgical procedures and denture additions.

a) Non-surgical periodontal treatment including root planing, deep scaling, irrigation of periodontal pockets and subgingival curettage and all necessary scaling and polishing

b) Surgical periodontal treatment including gingivectomy, gingivoplasty or removal of an operculum

c) Surgical periodontal treatment including raising and replacement of a mucoperiosteal flap, curettage, root planing and bone resection

d)   Free gingival grafts

e)   Permanent fillings in amalgam, composite resin, synthetic resin, glass ionomer, compomers, silicate or silico-phosphate, including acid etch retention

f)   Sealant restorations

g)   Endodontic treatment of permanent or retained deciduous teeth

h)   Pulpotomy

i)   Apicectomy

j)   Extraction of teeth

k)   Transplantation of teeth

l)   Oral surgery including surgical removal of cyst, buried root, unerupted tooth, impacted tooth or exostosed tooth and alveolectomy

m) Soft tissue surgery in relation to buccal cavity and lips

n)   Frenectomy, frenoplasty and frenotomy

o)   Relining and rebasing dentures including soft linings

p)   Addition of tooth, clasp, labial or buccal flange to dentures

q)   Splints (other than laboratory fabricated splints) in relation to periodontally compromised teeth and in connection with external trauma

r)   Bite raising appliances (other than laboratory fabricated appliances)

Band 3 (12 UDAs)

Complex treatment, which includes a laboratory element, such as bridgework, crowns, and dentures.

a)   Porcelain, composite or acrylic mastique veneers, including acid etch retention

b)   Inlays, pinlays, onlays and palatal veneers in alloys containing 60 per cent or more fine gold, porcelain, composite resin ceramics

c)   Full or ¾ crown cast in alloys containing not less than 33.3 per cent fine gold or platinum or palladium

d)   Full or jacket crown cast in alloys containing stainless steel or cobalt chromium or nickel chromium

e)   Crown in porcelain, synthetic resin and other non-metallic crowns

f)   Full or jacket crowns in alloys containing not less than 33.3 per cent fine gold or platinum or palladium or alloys containing stainless steel or cobalt chromium or nickel chromium with thermally bonded porcelain

g)   Jacket crown thermally bonded to wrought platinum coping

h)   Prefabricated full jacket crown, including any pin or post retention

This was deleted in July 2006 by the DH as it was considered a drafting error, in effect allowing crowns to be made in any material.

i)   Crowns in other materials

j)   Bridge in alloys containing 60 per cent or more fine gold with or without thermally bonded facings

k)   Bridges in cast alloys containing stainless steel, cobalt chromium or nickel chromium with or without thermally bonded facings

l)   Acid etch retained bridges

m) Bridges in other materials

n)   Provision of full (complete) or partial dentures, overdentures and obturators in synthetic resin or metal or both synthetic resin and metal, including any cast or wrought metal component or aids to retention

o)   Orthodontic treatment and appliances

p)   Other custom-made appliances excluding sports mouth guards

The charges regulations

R NHS (Dental Charges) Amendment 2005: Statutory Instrument 2005 No. 3477.

Note: This could change in Wales.

The Regulations were published in December 2005 and came into force on 1 April 2006. They can be modified from time to time and it is important to keep up to date with them. They specify when you can make NHS charges and, perhaps more important, when you cannot do this; in particular you cannot charge for a broken appointment. You (or the practice) collect the charge from the patient and then this is deducted from your monthly payment. It will be deducted whether or not the patient actually pays, so the onus is on you to make sure that patients pay. You can collect the charge in advance and this may be advisable if the patient is unknown to you or has a poor record of paying. This is probably discriminatory, but appears to be allowed.

You are entitled under the contract to refuse to begin a course of treatment or terminate a course of treatment prior to its completion if you have requested the appropriate payment under the charges regulations and the patient has failed to pay the charge.

R NHS (General Dental Services Contracts) 2005 ¶4 P1 S3.

Exemptions

Patients can be exempt from charges or treatment may not be chargeable. In addition patients may be eligible to have their charges 'remitted'. These can change and it is important that you keep up to date with current regulations.

These are listed in paragraph 1(1) of Schedule 12ZA to the Health and Social Care Act 2003 and can only be changed by Act of Parliament.

The following are exempt from dental charges if on the first day of treatment they are:

● patients under 18

● patients under 19 and in full-time education

● those who are pregnant

● patients who have had a baby within the previous 12 months.

Those who have charges remitted are basically those in receipt of certain welfare benefits and do not have to pay for NHS dental care because during the course of treatment they or their partner receive:

- Income Support
- Income-based Jobseekers Allowance
- Income-related Employment and Support Allowance
- Pension Credit Guarantee Credit

Patients are also entitled to free NHS dental services if they are named on an valid HC2 certificate or NHS tax credit exemption certificate during the course of treatment or they may be entitled to reduced costs if they are on an HC3 certificate

The patient is responsible for the accuracy of any declaration they make and routine checks are made where evidence of entitlement is shown to the dental practice. The practice makes a declaration if they have seen any evidence of entitlement from the patient and records this when making the claim. Where no evidence is provided or the practice is unclear if the evidence is valid they should indicate that no evidence was seen. If patients are found to have wrongly claimed free or reduced cost NHS dental services they are liable to a penalty charge of £100.

7 A DIFFERENT WAY OF WORKING

The 2006 contract marked an end to payment by item of service and the abolition of the 'Statement of Dental Remuneration' which laid down rules about what treatment could or could not be provided and, in some cases, the frequency with which it could be offered (the so-called time bars). Under the new system it is for you, the dentist, to decide what treatment options to offer patients and advise them what might be best for them as individuals. The *Framework Proposals*, however, laid down some general principles which should be your guide to the care provided under the new contract.

Framework Proposals for primary dental services in England from 2005. DH, ¶35.

- Treatment offered must be clinically necessary.
- Patients accepted as NHS patients who wish to undergo clinically necessary treatment must be able to receive this under the NHS if they wish.
- Patients must be able to exercise informed choice and must give valid consent to any treatment. Once accepted under the NHS, patients must be given the information necessary to make informed choices about their healthcare.
- Treatments that are cosmetic or requested for social reasons are not provided under the NHS, but may be offered privately.
- Patients should be encouraged to enter into a continuing relationship with their dentist, but those not wishing to do so should be offered such care and treatment as is appropriate, considering what they are willing to undergo.
- Prevention and the treatment of any underlying disease should be incorporated into any course of treatment.
- Modern teaching advocates a minimal intervention approach in many cases; such guidance should be followed.
- The prognosis of individual teeth and the mouth in general should be considered when offering complex forms of treatment.
- Treatment should be appropriate to the circumstances under which a patient seeks care, i.e. whether they are seeking emergency/urgent care or as a patient who attends regularly or as one who needs management for a chronic condition.

UNDERSTANDING NHS DENTISTRY

Although the regulations allow you wide latitude and clinical freedom you are expected to use this responsibility in the best interests of both the patient and the NHS. Your treatment patterns will be scrutinised by the Primary Care Trust to identify those dentists who are 'playing the UDA game' or 'gaming'. To give a simple example, NICE guidance on recall intervals allows you to recommend that an adult patient returns at appropriate intervals ranging from three months to two years. So if you have patients who are at high risk of developing caries or deteriorating periodontal disease, it is quite in order to recall them at three-month intervals, but these conditions will normally apply to relatively few patients. If you are recalling a large proportion of your patients at such a short interval, the PCT may well ask you to justify this.

Changes to patient care

The changes introduced by the Government were intended to move care from a treatment-based system to one which allowed dentists to use a more preventive approach, using a process of risk management. As then-Acting CDO Dr Barry Cockcroft put it in March 2006:

> **Dentists have been stuck on the same treadmill for far too long. These reforms to NHS dentistry set dentists free to spend more time with their patients and offer more preventative care.**

This is in line with modern teaching, which also lays stress on minimal intervention as a preferable approach. PCTs will also be responsible for commissioning dental public health services.

A new approach to dental fitness

Since 1948 the General Dental Services Regulations have required a dentist to render a patient dentally fit. Dentists have therefore examined their patients and prescribed such restorative treatments as are deemed necessary. Under the new arrangements there is a requirement to provide a range of mandatory dental services, but without the obligation to make the patient dentally fit.

It could be argued that the treatments prescribed under the old contract did not actually render a patient dentally fit. They restored form and function, but did not treat the underlying condition that led to the loss of tooth substance or periodontal attachment. There was virtually no provision in the pre-April 2006 regulations for the prevention of further disease. Caries and periodontal disease are both chronic conditions which should be approached in a similar way to chronic conditions elsewhere in the body.

GDS Contract, Clause 74.1.
GDS Contract, Clause 47.5.
GDS Contract, Clause 75.2.

What is required by Contractors is to provide all proper and necessary dental care and treatment…which is necessary to meet the reasonable needs of its patients. There is also a need to secure the oral health of the patient which is similar but not quite the same as the old requirement to achieve dental fitness. This is also subject to the patient agreeing to the treatment since they sign the following declaration on the FP17 and PR form:

> I would like the dental Provider named above, or their representative, to examine me under the NHS and to give me any necessary care and treatment that I am willing to undergo within NHS arrangements.

Managing chronic disease

The management of chronic diseases across healthcare gained a higher profile with the publication of a Department of Health paper which stated that chronic diseases 'are those that can only be controlled and not, at present, cured'. It also said that with the right support many people 'can learn to be active participants in their own care'.

Improving Chronic Disease Management. DH, March 2004.

The NHS has also recently introduced the concept of the 'expert patient', someone who has learnt about their condition and how to manage it, often with the active support of other sufferers. Some of our patients are already on their way to becoming 'expert patients'; but as a dental public health measure PCTs might wish to encourage this trend.

Although the Department of Health's paper applied to such conditions as arthritis, asthma and other respiratory diseases, diabetes and stroke, the same principles of patient self-management and prevention can apply to dental caries and periodontal disease, with the emphasis shifting away from treatment. The new arrangements should allow this to happen.

Risk factor approach to care

Dental Recall interval between routine dental examinations. NICE, October 2004.

The guideline on the recall interval by NICE is based on a preventive philosophy and recommends an individualised approach based on a risk assessment of the patient. The recommended recall interval for each patient will vary according to the dentist's assessment of their individual risk but is likely to extend in most cases beyond the 'standard' six months adopted in many practices.

The same principles can also apply to treatments, with interventions being less likely in 'low risk' patients and more likely in 'high risk' patients. This tendency was reinforced by the abolition of payment through fees for items of service. Dentists should be able to care for patients in the way most appropriate to their individual risk assessment.

Need versus demand

The healthcare issues in this area are increasingly complex: what a patient *needs* may not necessarily be the same as what the patient *wants* or *demands*. Patients do not have the right under the NHS contract to demand specific forms of treatment, the only criteria being whether the treatment is clinically necessary to secure their oral health and whether the treatment is likely to be long-lasting. Poor periodontal condition or mobility of teeth, for instance, would rule out many complex restorations.

Assessing a patient's needs covers the spectrum of 'needs', from an absolute necessity which patient and dentist both recognise, to a 'need' perceived by the patient and dentist which is not an absolute one. In very simplistic terms, pathological disease processes such as caries, periodontal disease and mucosal lesions require treatment and should be offered to the patient under NHS contract, while patients' wants, in the absence of disease process, may be provided outside the health service.

Kay E. *A Modern Concept of Oral Health.* Booklet 1. Denplan Dental Update Series, 2005.

To enable you to decide if a proposed treatment is available under the GDS Contract or whether it can be provided privately, your practice could draw up written protocols for the various treatments you may provide. These could be made available to your PCT in the event of your decision being queried.

Minimal intervention

↓ p66. As previously mentioned, the Government's *Framework Proposals* had this to say about minimal intervention:

> **Modern teaching advocates a minimal intervention approach in many cases; such guidance should be followed.**

Mjor *et al.* (2002). In 2002, Mjor and Gordan said that small defects of secondary caries, and stained and degraded margins may be removed by refurbishing/refinishing procedures. Larger defects may be explored by removing part of the restoration to access the defective margin. 'These approaches will save tooth structure and be cost-effective,' the authors wrote.

Repair of restorations is in general considered a more conservative treatment option, which in addition to saving time may increase the long-term survival of the tooth, and in some situations may be performed without Mjor (1993). the use of local anaesthesia and therefore prove less distressing for patients. The evidence regarding the effectiveness of repair versus replacement of amalgam and composite restorations is, however, weak and incomplete: Sharif *et al.* (2010). clinical decision-making in this area will continue to be very subjective.

The Cochrane Oral Health Group has published a review on the efficacy of routine scale and polishes for periodontal health in adults. They found, however, that the research evidence was of insufficient quality to reach any conclusions regarding the beneficial and adverse effects of routine scaling and polishing for periodontal health and regarding the effects of provid- Beirne *et al.* (2005). ing this intervention at different time intervals.

The modern management of caries requires a more biological approach to be adopted which includes, first, its early diagnosis, and then management through changing the local biochemical conditions by:

- changing the microflora, using agents such as topical chlorhexidine and topical fluoride
- reducing the amount of dietary sucrose, by dietary choice
- decreasing the frequency of eating, by dietary choice
- adding fluoride, particularly through daily application during tooth brushing
- increasing salivary flow, using mechanical stimulation during vigorous chewing to enhance flow, by changing drugs which reduce flow, or by using drugs to enhance flow.

www.midentistry.org
Mount *et al.* (2005).

The cure is achieved when diagnostic tests show that the disease is no longer active and the risk is low. The concepts of minimal intervention dentistry are being championed by a number of organisations such as Minimal Intervention Dentistry and individuals such as Graham Mount and Geoff Knight.

Unplanned care

Adult Dental Health Survey, 1998.

About two-thirds of the population say they visit their dentist on a regular basis, although this is their subjective view of what constitutes 'regular' care: it could be once every six months or once every six years. The other third attend 'only when in pain'. In addition anyone may develop some problem and need unplanned care. About half the population report that they have a dentally related problem each year. Previously, those registered with a dentist were entitled to such care and were fitted into appointment books as an emergency.

Those not registered under the old system often experienced serious problems in accessing such care. Under the current arrangements the distinction between registered and unregistered has ceased, as has the obligation to see registered patients for emergency treatment. Dentists are, however, encouraged to see their 'regular patients' and, if they have spare capacity, to accept new patients, perhaps those requiring 'urgent care'.

Clinical care pathways and recall intervals

The concept of clinical care pathways was set out in the Department of Health's report *Options for Change* (2002). The Department envisaged these pathways as being:

a documented sequence of effective clinical interventions, placed in a appropriate time frame, written and agreed by a multi-disciplinary team. They help a patient with a specific condition or diagnosis move progressively through clinical experience to the desired outcome.

The NHS Oral Health Assessment. April 2006 (GR 6503). Department of Health.

The Dental Health Services Research Unit (DHSRU) at the University of Dundee under the guidance of Professor Nigel Pitts developed the pathways and its final report was published in April 2006. The algorithms are complex and not yet IT-based and thus not yet of practical use. Once in use, however, the gateway to NHS dentistry will be through a standard Oral Health Assessment comprising three elements:

- **Diagnosis**
  This provides recommendations for treatment to the patient where necessary, setting out on a standard estimate form the patient's state of oral health and what treatment options are available under NHS arrangements.

- **Prevention**
  This includes lifestyle advice such as smoking cessation, oral health, oral cancer screening.

- **Treatment planning**
  The options available both under NHS and private contract should be discussed.

The basic components of the clinical care pathway are:

- diagnosis
- needs assessment
- prevention
- care options discussed
- oral healthcare provided
- oral health review.

NICE guidance on recall intervals

When a course of treatment is completed, the patient needs to be assessed to establish their next date for a recall examination, based on NICE guidelines. Clause 71 of the Standard Contract, as well as the Regulations, make adherence to NICE guidance mandatory:

> **The Contractor shall provide services under the contract in accordance with any relevant guidance that is issued by the National Institute for Clinical Excellence, in particular the guidance entitled 'Dental Recall – recall interval between routine dental examinations'.**

Ⓡ NHS (General Dental Services Contracts) 2005, ¶14 P2.

The guidance from NICE suggests that the recommended interval between 'oral health reviews' – the new name for check-ups – should be determined specifically for each patient and tailored to meet his or her needs on the basis of an assessment of disease levels and risk from dental disease.

The traditional six-monthly recall has little evidence to support its continued use for all patients and recall intervals need to be based on individual risk assessment. However, a study reviewing a number of trials concluded that:

> There is insufficient evidence from randomised controlled trials to draw any conclusions regarding the potential beneficial and harmful effects of altering the recall interval between dental check-ups. There is insufficient evidence to support or refute the practice of encouraging patients to attend for dental check-ups at six monthly intervals.

Mettes (2006).

From a practical point of view it is important to risk assess each patient for caries, periodontal disease, mucosal lesions and malocclusion.

Traffic light indicators

Using this information a traffic light system can be adopted and used on patients' notes highlighting their risk category for a specific problem. In this system *high risk* patients are denoted by a red circle, *medium risk* by an amber circle and *low risk* by a green circle.

CG19, 'Modifying factors checklist': *www.nice.org.uk.*

The checklist of modifying factors is available from the NICE website. This breaks them down into the following categories:

- medical history
- social history
- dietary habits
- exposure to fluoride
- clinical evidence of caries and dental history of caries
- recent and previous periodontal disease and experience
- mucosal lesions
- plaque levels
- saliva flow rate
- erosion and tooth surface loss.

⬧ p 73. In our version shaded boxes represent factors that may increase a patient's risk of or from oral disease.

The PCT would expect practitioners to adopt this risk assessment approach and demonstrate evidence that it is being implemented. Where patients continue to be recalled at six-monthly intervals without appropriate risk assessments the PCT would be entitled to invoke Clause 71 and expect adherence to it. PCTs are most likely to do this where they have an access problem and patients are experiencing difficulty accessing NHS services. They may also do this where practices are seeking growth funding, having used up all their UDA allocation.

NHS Executive Clinical Guidelines *Leeds NHSE 1996:10.*

Ultimately the NICE guidelines are simply that – guidelines. Clinical guidelines can still only assist the practitioner; they cannot be used to mandate, authorise or outlaw treatment options. Regardless of the strength of the evidence, it will remain your responsibility to interpret their application.

Oral health review date:						
Medical history	Yes	No	Yes	No	Yes	No
Conditions where dental disease could put the patient's general health at increased risk (such as cardiovascular disease, bleeding disorders, immunosuppression)	☐	☐	☐	☐	☐	☐
Conditions that increase a patient's risk of developing dental disease (such as diabetes, xerostomia)	☐	☐	☐	☐	☐	☐
Conditions that may complicate dental treatment or the patient's ability to maintain their oral health (such as special needs, anxious/nervous/phobic conditions)	☐	☐	☐	☐	☐	☐
Social history						
High caries in mother and siblings	☐	☐	☐	☐	☐	☐
Tobacco use	☐	☐	☐	☐	☐	☐
Excessive alcohol use	☐	☐	☐	☐	☐	☐
Family history of chronic or aggressive (early onset/juvenile) periodontitis	☐	☐	☐	☐	☐	☐
Dietary habits						
High and/or frequent sugar intake	☐	☐	☐	☐	☐	☐
High and/or frequent dietary acid intake	☐	☐	☐	☐	☐	☐
Exposure to fluoride						
Use of fluoride toothpaste	☐	☐	☐	☐	☐	☐
Other sources of fluoride (for example, lives in a water-fluoridated area)	☐	☐	☐	☐	☐	☐
Clinical evidence and dental history						
Recent and previous caries experience						
New lesions since last check-up	☐	☐	☐	☐	☐	☐
Anterior caries or restorations	☐	☐	☐	☐	☐	☐
Premature extractions because of caries	☐	☐	☐	☐	☐	☐
Past root caries or large number of exposed roots	☐	☐	☐	☐	☐	☐
Heavily restored dentition	☐	☐	☐	☐	☐	☐
Recent and previous periodontal disease experience						
Previous history of periodontal disease	☐	☐	☐	☐	☐	☐
Evidence of gingivitis	☐	☐	☐	☐	☐	☐
Presence of periodontal pockets (BPE code 3 or 4) and/or bleeding on probing	☐	☐	☐	☐	☐	☐
Presence of furcation involvements or advanced attachment loss (BPE code; that is, attachment loss is at least 7 mm and/or furcation involvements are present)	☐	☐	☐	☐	☐	☐
Mucosal lesions						
Mucosal lesion present	☐	☐	☐	☐	☐	☐
Plaque						
Poor level of oral hygiene	☐	☐	☐	☐	☐	☐
Plaque-retaining factors (such as orthodontic appliances)	☐	☐	☐	☐	☐	☐
Saliva						
Low saliva flow rate	☐	☐	☐	☐	☐	☐
Erosion and tooth surface loss						
Clinical evidence of tooth wear	☐	☐	☐	☐	☐	☐
Recommended recall interval for next oral health review:	... months		... months		... months	
Does patient agree with recommended interval? (If 'No' record reason for disagreement in notes overleaf)	Yes	No	Yes	No	Yes	No

Interestingly in a survey, only half of general dental practitioners agreed that they were able to apply NICE guidance to recalls, but only a quarter (24.2%) felt that they had clinical freedom under the new contract

Chestnutt *et al.* (2009).

As there is no ready reckoner, practitioners may have difficulty in interpreting the information in the NICE guidelines and applying it consistently and methodically in practice, especially since the guidance is particularly wordy and non-specific. A recent article is intended to remedy this with the provision of Codes to help relate risks to suitable recall intervals.

Akram *et al.* (2010).

Phased approach to treatment

One of the most significant problems with the old pre-April 2006 contract was that the fee-per-item remuneration method meant that clinical treatment on patients was driven by what was available on the Statement of Dental Remuneration. While there may have been over 400 items on the list, it came with provisos as to when each item could be claimed, and under what circumstances. Therefore, if there was no fee code, that particular treatment was generally not available on the NHS. There was no flexibility in the system and some treatments required Prior Approval from the Dental Practice Board. There is no Prior Approval in the 2006 contract, nor is there a detailed and prescriptive list of what is and what is not available on the NHS. It also means that the time bars for examination intervals and periodontal treatment no longer exist. This provides an opportunity to change the way care is delivered to patients, without necessarily impacting on your NHS income.

Adopting problem-based treatment planning skills leads to a more systematic method of treating patients which translates itself into a phased approach to clinical care. This ensures that, first, the patients' problems become the focus of treatment planning and, second, in terms of overall health gain, complex treatments are not provided until basic corrective treatment is provided and the patient responds favourably to preventive techniques.

A problem list is a numbered list of identified problems, with each problem listed on a separate line, with a column to the right allowing classification into 'active' and 'inactive' problems. An **active problem** is one that will be addressed within the present treatment plan and **inactive problem** is a variance from the norm, which is to be monitored but does not need active treatment within the present treatment plan.

Bain (2003).

Crawford Bain, in his book *Treatment Planning in General Dental Practice*, summarises the fundamental principles in planning the order in which treatment should be provided to patients, and this is particularly true of new patients presenting to the practice who have a number of different problems. Table 4 (adapted from Bain's book) summarises this phased approach.

▶ p 75.

Phase	Rationale	Treatments
Relief of pain and other emergencies	Relieves patient's immediate pain problems to enable them to return for definitive treatments	● Pulp extirpation ● Caries removal and sedative dressing ● Extraction ● Irrigation and mouthwash ● Prescription ● Re-cementation of crowns, bridges and other restorations
Cause-related therapy	Focuses on the cause rather than the effects of disease	● Plaque control instruction ● Diet counselling ● Fluoride advice ● Smoking cessation advice ● Fissure sealing ● Calculus removal and root planing ● Dressing of active carious lesions ● Removal of overhangs
Initial reassessment	Ensures that proper stock is taken of the prognosis of doubtful teeth, initial compliance with homecare advice and to finalise the basic treatment plan	
Basic corrective care	Designed to repair or minimise the damage caused by disease processes	● Endodontics on strategically important teeth ● Placement of plastic restorations ● Provisional crowns, bridges and interim dentures to address aesthetic concerns ● Splinting of teeth ● Extraction of hopeless and non-strategic teeth
Pre-constructive therapy	Basic therapies required for the definitive final reconstruction where appropriate	● Elective endodontics ● Periodontal surgery for restorative purposes such as crown lengthening
Reconstructive therapy	Fabrication and placement of all definitive restorations usually involving laboratory work	● Crowns ● Bridges ● Partial dentures
Recall and maintenance care		

Table 4: A phased approach to treatment.

FGDP (2003).

This approach is similar to that advocated in the Faculty of General Dental Practitioners' *Pathways in Practice* (2003). Chapter 5 (on treatment planning) was written by Philip Newsome, who says:

> any treatment plan, to be successful, must incorporate short, medium and long-term views and must take a holistic view of the patient as a person to be cared for, not just a mouth to be fixed.

What many authors advocate is a phased approach to treatment planning, a 'smooth and logical progression through the various treatment phases', to quote *Pathways in Practice*.

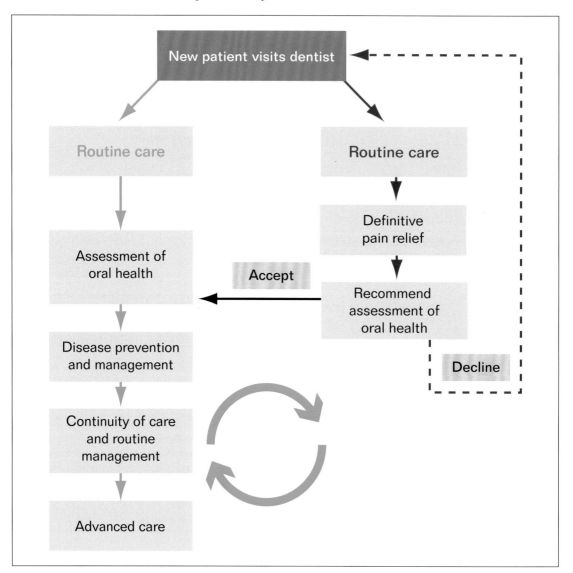

Figure 13: Treatment pathway (taken from *NHS Dental Services – an independent review led by Professor Steele*. June 2009 (GR 12070).

Standard undergraduate textbooks also teach treatment planning in stages:

1) **Urgent treatment** for the relief of pain or other symptoms.

2) **Stabilization** of progressive disease or conditions which may become acute (e.g. temporarily restore very carious teeth, remove necrotic pulps or extract teeth even if they are symptomless at the time).

3) Assess the cause of the dental disease and begin initial **preventive measures**.

4) **Reassess** the patient response to this initial treatment and decide the broad outline of the future plan based on the patients motivation, their response to initial treatment and preventive measures and the cost.

5) Provide the **initial stages of definitive treatment** which may be further preventive measures, periodontal treatment. Orthodontic treatment, extractions or other surgical treatment.

6) A further **reassessment** to evaluate the success of the first stage of treatment and revise the treatment plan as necessary.

7) Provide the **final stages of the active course of treatment** such as crown and dentures.

8) Reassessment, maintenance and reinforcement of preventive measures.

Kidd et al. (2003) p 46..

This stepwise approach is supported by the leading indemnity organisation in the UK, Dental Protection. This is in keeping with the proposed pathway in the Steele Report (Figure 13).

Taking steps Riskwise UK. March 2009. (Dental Protection Limited)

Treatment gates

Singh (2007).

The Department of Health envisages 'treatment lock' which prevent patients accessing more complex care unless basic parameters of health can be demonstrated. This approach could well be developed in the next contract.

For example a patient with active carious lesions, high BPE scores and social history risk factors such as poor diet and high alcohol intake may be placed in the 'red zone' of a risk categorisation preventing further high value treatment being given on the basis that it would not be cost effective.

This Advanced restorative care includes

- complete dentures
- molar endodontics
- minor oral surgery
- treatment of aggressive or advanced periodontal conditions
- straightforward orthodontics
- implant retained overdentures
- multiple crowns, bridges and occlusal rehabilitation.

Rather than 'locks', as described by the Department, we would envisage these barriers to more advanced care as 'gates': it is, after all, the patient who has control of their own health goals and who, with suitable support and encouragement, will have the necessary drive to open the gates to long-term care and definitive restorations.

In the old GDS a treatment plan and a course of treatment were synonymous; in the new GDS an overall care plan may consist of a number of courses of treatment. This approach to treatment planning is based on sound clinical principles and has been accepted by the NHS as good practice. It should not, however, be undertaken as a means of artificially breaking up treatment in order to 'play the UDA game'. By using and understanding the principles it will be easier for you to defend your stance if challenged: UDA 'gaming', in contrast, could not be defended in such a challenge.

8 SERVICES & COURSES OF TREATMENT

Mandatory services

Under the old GDS there was a clear 'list' of what should or should not be provided. To a large extent the 2006 contract leaves this to your clinical judgement, subject to any constraints that may be written into your contract. The care you offer must be necessary to secure oral health and should be within your competence; if not, you should refer the patient. You are expected to provide all proper and necessary treatment which a dentist usually undertakes and which the patient is willing to undergo. There is no Prior Approval.

GDS Contracts require that you provide 'mandatory services' for your patients. These must be carried out at the practice during normal surgery hours. 'Normal hours' are defined quite simply as the times at which the Contractor has agreed with the PCT (and specified in the contract) that the surgery will be open to patients for the provision of services – in other words, any hours the practice and PCT believe are reasonable.

Mandatory services include urgent treatment carried out during these hours or hours that you have specified to the PCT. The care and treatment covered by mandatory services include:

- examination, radiographs, diagnosis, advice and planning of treatment
- preventive care and treatment
- periodontal treatment
- conservative treatment
- surgical treatment
- supply and repair of dental appliances
- supply of listed drugs and the issue of prescriptions.

Mandatory services do not include additional services (described below) or treatments (such as implants) which are not normally provided in

NHS primary care. General anaesthetics cannot be provided under a GDS Contract.

Additional services

Additional services can be added to a GDS Contract by agreement with the PCT. The dentist will have to agree to provide a specified number of such services and the PCT will have to agree how much will be paid for these. These include one or more of the following:

- advanced mandatory services
- orthodontics
- dental public health services
- domiciliary services
- sedation.

Advanced mandatory services

Advanced mandatory services are mandatory services which require a 'high level of facilities, experience or expertise' for a particular patient. These could include complex surgical, endodontic, periodontal or prosthetic cases and might well be carried out by a dentist on the General Dental Council's Specialist Register or a Dentist with a Special Interest. They could also mean a second opinion if requested by the patient or taking a panoral radiograph.

Advanced mandatory services are provided as a referral service. Such referrals must be done formally, but there is nothing to prevent referral within the same practice. There will be a limit to the number of referrals that can be made and paid for by the PCT. A practice might 'refer' all its endodontic cases or dentures to one practitioner, but could not claim that they were all 'advanced mandatory services'. You are expected to be able to do uncomplicated procedures yourself; it is the more complex cases that would be called advanced mandatory services.

What is complex treatment?

Who determines whether a particular treatment requires a high level of facilities, experience or expertise? To an extent you do, as you have a professional duty not to undertake treatment that is beyond your competence. If, however, a reasonably skilled general dental practitioner would be expected to carry out the treatment, questions about your competence may be raised.

Royal College of Surgeons (2001).

Muthukrishnan *et al.* (2007).

There are some guidelines available to help in this area. The Restorative Dentistry Index of Treatment Need Complexity Assessment covers root canal treatment, periodontal assessment, fixed prosthodontics and removable prothodontics. Muthukrishnan *et al.* have also set out guidance for root canal treatment complexity, while the British Society of Periodontology have set out when they feel it is appropriate to treat or refer.

www.bsperio.org.uk/members/referral.htm

Domiciliary and sedation services

You can agree to provide domiciliary services or sedation as part of a course of treatment or on referral. If you agree with your PCT that you will provide these services you will be contracted to provide a set number each year. If you offer sedation you must do so in accordance with the recommendations contained in the report of the Standing Dental Advisory Committee entitled *Conscious Sedation in the Provision of Dental Care.*

www.dh.gov.uk/en/
Publicationsandstatistics/Publications/
PublicationsPolicyAndGuidance/DH_
4069257

Courses of treatment

Care is delivered to patients as 'courses of treatment' – these can be considered to be discrete units of care which, clinically, will have defined objectives. A 'course of treatment' is defined as:

> an examination of a patient, an assessment of his oral health, and the planning of any treatment to be provided to that patient as a result of that examination and assessment, and the provision of any planned treatment (including any treatment planned at a time other than the time of the initial examination) to that patient.

R P1(2).

(To reiterate: there is no continuing NHS relationship with patients between courses of treatment as existed with registration and the attendant registration and capitation payments in the old contract.)

Having accepted a patient for a course of treatment you must make an assessment of their oral health and provide a written treatment plan, unless it is for examination, radiographs or scaling only.

This treatment plan must define the extent of care provided in that course, and all the treatment recommended and agreed with the patient should be provided and completed within a reasonable time. The FP17 claim form or its electronic equivalent must be sent for payment within two months of the completion of treatment.

If you accept a patient for urgent treatment, this will constitute a course of treatment in itself and no other services can be provided.

Termination of a course of treatment

If a course of treatment has a beginning, it must have an end. The end most often will be when the defined course of treatment (in the written treatment plan where appropriate) has been provided to the patient.

If the patient fails to complete the course of treatment, you must indicate this when the form is sent off, together with the reason. If you are terminating a course of treatment where there is still outstanding treatment to be completed it is important that the patient is made aware that if they return after the form is sent off then any outstanding treatment will have to be provided as a new course. This will mean a further charge if the patient is a fee paying adult.

R S3 P2 6(4).

In order to avoid complaints and manage the process of sending off claims for incomplete treatment a sensible practice management protocol would be to send a letter to the patient, advising them of the consequences of not completing their treatment. Below is a suggested letter which can be used when a patient has not returned to the practice for the completion of their treatment.

Dear [Patient],

On reviewing our records we note that you have not returned to the practice for completion of your NHS dental treatment since [date last seen].

The NHS allows us a short time within which to process the paperwork and therefore I would be grateful if you could contact the practice to make an appointment to complete any outstanding treatment.

If we do not hear from you by [date 7–14 days in future] I will assume you do not wish to complete this course of treatment and we will send off the NHS forms.

If you return after the forms have been processed, we will need to provide any treatment as a new course of treatment and you will need to pay the appropriate charge band unless you are exempt from dental charges.

Yours sincerely,

[A Dentist]

Units of Dental Activity

Units of Dental Activity (UDAs) have proved a highly controversial measure of output in the new contract. The Health Committee said that their introduction as the measure of dental activity and the basis for remunerating dentists was extremely unpopular with dentists. In the PDS pilots that preceded the introduction of the contract there were no consistent measures of activity. The Department of Health took the view that, for the new contract, it was reasonable to define activity levels by reference to courses of treatment, weighted to reflect their complexity.

House of Commons Health Committee: Dental Services Fifth Report of Session 2007–08 paragraph 175

So UDAs are, in fact, courses of treatment. Their complexity is measured by reference to the banding system of patients' charges. The Government

◆ Chapter 6, 'Patients', pp 61–4.

believed that the new system would lead to simpler courses of treatment and more time available to adopt a more preventive approach. Some dentists reject this line of thinking but there have been

> **significant changes in treatment patterns resulting from the more preventive approach encouraged by the new contracts [which] have reduced overall treatment complexity.**

Written Evidence from the UK Health Departments to the Review Body on Doctors' and Dentists' Remuneration: Review for 2009, ¶29.

UDAs have different values which are a matter for negotiation between Contractor and PCT. In this they differ from Units of Orthodontic Activity which are of a fixed value across the country. UDAs differ from PCT to PCT and from practice to practice and may be decided through a tendering process, especially as far as additional activity is concerned. The differences come about because they relate to activity under the old contract. Under that system a practice seeing patients who had high needs and required more treatment earned more per patient than those practices whose patients had lower needs. The cost per course of treatment (known then as cost per estimate) would be higher in the first practice compared with the second. In addition, the cost per estimate in a high cost area, such as London, tended to be higher than in low cost areas.

The 'cost per estimate' formed the basis of the UDA value. It is quite logical, therefore, that UDA values should differ between PCTs to reflect differences in costs such as property rental values and staff wages. PCTs on the whole understand this concept, but you may have more trouble convincing them that it is also logical for UDA values to differ between practices (or in some cases within practices). However, if you are seeing patients with higher treatment needs you will have higher costs per course of treatment and you should have a higher UDA value.

Statutory Instrument 2005 No. 3435: The General Dental Services and Personal Dental Services Transitional Provisions Order 2005.

The method of calculating the number of UDAs to be completed was contained in the Transitional Provisions Order. Although the calculations were made by the then Dental Practice Board, the Order laid on the PCT a duty to analyse the work done by the dentist(s) concerned during the test year, 1 October 2004 to 30 September 2005. The PCT was to categorise this work according to the charge bands into which the treatment came and then calculate the number of UDAs required from the dentist. The PCT was told to make an assumption that, for every under 18 year old registered, two examinations had taken place during the test year. Finally the PCT was told to reduce the number of UDAs calculated by 5 per cent to give a final number to be provided in each financial year.

Many felt that this method of calculation was unfair, especially for those who had only needed to carry out an examination once a year on children and found themselves unable to meet their UDA requirements, especially if they had a contract for children only. It needs to be understood that the Transitional Provisions Order applied only to the initial calculation of UDA requirement. A PCT may well argue that it no longer applies after the 'guaranteed period' expired in March 2009. In forthcoming years they (and dentists) may wish to vary the number of UDAs required to reflect the practising patterns of each individual practice.

There has been widespread criticism that the UDA is not suitable as the sole measure of activity. The British Dental Association has lobbied hard for the removal of UDAs as the sole contract monitoring since 2007. The Department of Health, in its response to the Health Committee, said there was 'a growing number of examples of innovative commissioning' not just involving UDAs, but believes that such an approach needs to be developed at PCT level rather than being imposed from above. It is true, however, that many associates continue to be paid on the basis of UDAs, making the latter into an item of service – something for which it was not designed.

Government Response to the Health Select Committee Report on Dental Services (26-28), October 2008 Cm 7470.

Your contract will specify the number of units of dental activity to be provided by you in the year from April until the following March. If you provide a banded course of treatment, you will be credited with the following units:

Table 5: UDAs credited for banded courses of treatment.

Type of course of treatment	UDAs provided
Band 1 course of treatment (excluding urgent treatment)	1.0
Band 1 course of treatment (urgent treatment only)	1.2
Band 2 course of treatment	3.0
Band 3 course of treatment	12.0

These values apply even if the patient is exempt from charges, including children.

For charge-exempt courses of treatment, the following UDAs will be credited to you.

Table 6: UDAs credited for charge-exempt courses of treatment.

Type of charge-exempt course of treatment	UDAs provided
Issue of a prescription	0.75
Repair of a dental appliance (denture)	1.0
Repair of a dental appliance (bridge)	1.2
Removal of sutures	1.0
Arrest of bleeding	1.2

For orthodontic courses of treatment, the following UOAs will be credited to you, but you can only claim them if provision of orthodontics is included in your contract.

Table 7: UOAs credited by course of treatment.

Type of orthodontic course of treatment	UOAs provided
Case assessment only	1.0
Case assessment and orthodontic treatment for under 18s	20.0
Case assessment and orthodontic treatment for 18 and over	22.0
Repair to an orthodontic appliance	0.8

(Note that orthodontic repairs only attract UOAs if the treatment is being carried out by another practice; for your own patients a repair does not attract any additional UOAs.)

Band 1 Urgent category

The category of Band 1 Urgent has caused some confusion, especially if it is followed by a second course of treatment. Urgent treatment is defined as prompt care and treatment provided because

> **the person's oral health is likely to deteriorate significantly, or the person is in severe pain by reason of his oral condition [...]**

and treatment is provided

> **only to the extent that it is necessary to prevent that significant deterioration or address that severe pain.**

Ⓡ NHS (Dental Charges) Amendment 2005: Statutory Instrument 2005 No. 3477.

You see a patient in pain, place a dressing and then subsequently fill the tooth. Does this count as one course of treatment (3 UDAs) or two courses of treatment (1.2 and 3 UDAs)? Are you 'playing the system' if you claim the latter, and should the patient have to pay two charges for what they may consider is only one course of treatment?

There is no simple answer to this dilemma: it is an area where you need to use your judgement and pay attention to what the patient wants. Take three (of many) possible scenarios.

1) One of your 'regular' patients asks for a routine appointment and mentions that they are having some trouble. It would be reasonable to attend to their problem on a temporary basis and then see them back to complete their all their treatment (3 UDAs).

2) Another dentist's patient asks to be seen as an emergency as their dentist is on holiday (1.2 UDAs).

3) A patient, whom you have not seen before, asks for urgent treatment, which you provide (1.2 UDAs) and then asks if you will 'do anything else that needs doing'. This would constitute a new course of treatment (either 3 or 12 UDAs).

If you refer a patient to another dentist for part of that course of treatment, say a surgical extraction, then each of you can claim the appropriate UDAs – 3.0 for the surgical extraction, 1.0, 3.0, 12.0 for you, depending on what other treatment was provided. The patient, however, only pays one charge for the whole course of treatment.

Where a course of treatment is started but not completed, the number of UDAs provided will be calculated on the basis of the complete course of treatment, as specified in their treatment plan, whether or not all of that treatment has been provided. However, if the number of treatments uncompleted is excessive, the PCT may challenge you on the reasons.

The PCT may take action if you fail to provide the UDAs you agreed for the year. It cannot take any action, however, if this failure amounts to 4 per cent or less of the total agreed. In the last resort the sanctions could mean termination of the contract. However, your PCT cannot take this action if you agree to make up the units within a time period of not less than 60 days.

If you are well behind your quota of UDAs, your PCT will want to discuss this with you. There may be valid reasons why this happens: for instance, if you have had a period of sickness or an associate has left and it has taken a long time to find a replacement. The PCT could decide not to vary the contract, if it feels that it was a one-off. Alternatively, the PCT can vary the number of UDAs you are required to deliver under your contract with a change in the contract value. First, however, you and the PCT must discuss the issue and try to come to an agreed way forward. In the words of the Regulations, 'both parties shall use their best endeavours to communicate and cooperate with each other with a view to determining what (if any) variation' in UDAs is needed.

Repair or replacement of restorations

The rules for repair or replacement of restorations within a 12-month period are substantially the same under the 2006 contract as under the old one. The patient should not be charged again, but the repair or replacement will count towards your quota of UDAs. For the purposes of this 'guarantee' the only restorations covered are:

- fillings
- root fillings
- inlays
- porcelain veneers
- crowns.

If the patient returns within two months following the completion of a course of treatment they are able to have treatment within the same band as the completed course without further charge and you are able to claim further UDAs. This guarantee does not apply if:

- another Provider other than yourself carried out the original restoration
- the patient was advised at the time you did the restoration, and one of the following was recorded in the clinical notes:
  - the restoration was temporary
  - a different form of restoration was more appropriate but the patient insisted, against your advice, to have that restoration
  - the repair or replacement is required as a result of trauma.

This is a complex area with many variables, so you may need to seek advice.

Making referrals

It is both a GDC requirement and an NHS contractual requirement that where a patient requires referral for services that the dentist is not able to provide, a referral should be made.

Referral to other practitioners: Collection of patient charges and assignment of units of dental activity. Factsheet 13. March 2006 (GR 5917). Department of Health.

When a patient is referred for additional services, including advanced mandatory services – that is, to a Performer who has an NHS contract with the PCT – there is an established route. This requires appropriate documentation to ensure that the correct number of UDAs are claimed and the correct patient charge is levied. This system will not apply when the patient is referred to a hospital or under private contract. It is also not intended to apply either when the practitioner to whom the referral is made does not have an additional services or advanced mandatory services contract with the PCT.

Scenario A – Patient referred for an entire course of treatment

When the referral is for an entire course of treatment:

- The referring practitioner will be credited with the appropriate UDAs for any treatment that has been provided up that point of referral – and the patient (if not exempt) will pay the appropriate charge for that course of treatment.
- The practitioner carrying out the new course of treatment will be credited with the appropriate UDAs or UOAs for that course of treatment – and the patient (if liable) will pay the appropriate charge for that band.

This often applies when the patient is seen by the dentist for an examination and then requests or requires all their treatment to be carried out under sedation or requires an orthodontic assessment or treatment which the dentist is unable to provide. It also applies where the patient requires domiciliary care.

Scenario B – Patient referred for part of a course of treatment

This scenario applies to referrals for advanced mandatory services, where the referring dentist lacks the required experience, expertise or facilities to provide a particular item of treatment for a particular patient.

Where a patient is being referred to another service for part of the treatment, i.e. when this is required as part of an overall course of treatment, the patient pays only one patient charge:

- The referring dentist will set out the patient's entire treatment plan and collect the patient charges associated with this overall course of treatment.
- The responsibility for collecting the patient charge will rest with the referring dentist.
- The dentist providing treatment on referral therefore collects no patient charges from the patient.

In relation to the UDAs, the referring dentist will be credited with the UDAs associated with the overall course of treatment. The dentist providing the additional service will be credited with the UDAs associated with the banded course of treatment provided as the additional service.

On the FP17 the referring dentist will complete Part 5 putting a cross in the box to indicate the band – most likely Band 2 – as well as a cross in the box in part 6 'Treatment on referral', ensuring also that the amount collected is shown in the patient charge collected in Part 4 of the form.

The dentist providing the treatment on referral does all of the above but leaves the patient charge collected box in Part 4 blank as they will not have collected any money from the patient, this having been done by the referring dentist.

This referral would potentially result in double-counting of UDAs: the Department of Health advice sheet to the PCTs warns of the need for robust protocols to ensure that referrals for advanced mandatory services are appropriate. NHS Dental Services will collect, analyse and report this data to the PCT.

Mixing private and NHS care

The NHS Information Centre published its survey of Dental Earnings and Expenses for England and Wales 2006–07 in September 2008. Figures showed that 19 per cent were in mainly private practice, 16 per cent in mixed NHS/private practice and 65 per cent in mainly NHS practice. (When asked the extent of their NHS commitment fewer than half of dentists – 48.75 per cent – responded. Some caution is therefore needed in assessing the significance of these statistics.) Private treatment, whether as a capitation patient or on a course of treatment basis, is outside the NHS regulations. A patient who is 'usually' seen under the NHS can be accepted, with their agreement, for a private course of treatment: this does not have to be notified to the PCT. The CDO has predicted a future where the NHS provides treatment to satisfy dental needs such as fillings and the private sector is focused on what may be termed 'lifestyle' dental treatments of a cosmetic nature such as teeth whitening. In evidence to the Health Select Committee he foresaw:

> a more complementary relationship between private dentistry, which is providing that service need for patients that is not actually properly covered by the NHS...the fancy cosmetic stuff and stuff like that...but the NHS providing healthcare, and that is what I think the future will be.

Problems may arise if you want to offer private treatment within an NHS course of treatment. You may, with the consent of the patient, provide any part of a course of treatment privately. Just as under the old contract, you must neither advise a patient that necessary services are not available under the NHS nor try to mislead the patient about the quality of the services available under the NHS. The treatment you offer privately is an alternative to the necessary treatment that you must offer under the NHS.

Ⓡ S3 ¶9.

There may, however, be some dispute over what is or is not necessary. Back in 2002 the Audit Commission said most people would agree that cosmetic activity should not be available on the NHS. But it said that a major difficulty with dental care lay 'in defining exactly what is necessary *health*care, and what is of cosmetic value'. It also claimed that 'large amounts of NHS money' were in fact being spent on cosmetic rather than health needs. It also gave some examples of treatments that were poor value for money, including scale and polishes, orthodontics, too many fillings being done and poor quality restorations leading to frequent replacements.

Primary dental care services in England and Wales Audit Commission September 2002

The real challenge in the 2006 contract, in the absence of prescriptive rules and the Statement of Dental Remuneration fee guide, is the exercise of clinical judgement, the clear communication of this to the patient and the making of good clinical notes. You must not mislead patients by saying that something is not available under the NHS, when in fact it is. Since everything is technically available on the NHS, including posterior composites, it is important that you understand the parameters of care within which NHS services should be provided.

Asking the questions

You have three options in this area and ultimately it is for the patient to choose which is best for them. You can carry out the treatment under the NHS; you can carry it out privately; in some circumstances, you should refer the case to another practitioner. To guide you in this, there are a number of questions you should ask.

● **Do you have a contract to provide this service?**
In most cases you will have, but some additional services such as orthodontics, domiciliary visits and sedation may not be included in your contract.

● **Is the proposed treatment within your competence?**
If you have a patient who needs a 'high level of facilities, experience or expertise' which you are unable to provide, then you should consider referring to a dentist who can provide 'advanced mandatory services' or into secondary care.

● **Are there any medical contraindications?**
These may influence the care that you recommend or may lead you to refer the patient.

● **Is the proposed treatment going to address the patient's health needs or is it only for cosmetic reasons?**
In many cases this will be the key question. Tooth whitening, the placement of veneers to improve the patient's appearance are obvious examples of cosmetic treatments. You need to ask yourself: 'Am I doing this treatment to improve their oral health or to improve their appearance?' If for oral health then it should be done under the NHS; if to improve appearance then it is private. Unfortunately not all cases are so clear cut.

● **Will the proposed treatment be clinically effective?**
Will it address the patient's oral health problems? Will it do more good than harm? These are the criteria that should guide you in offering a treatment under the NHS. The patient should be advised if there is the possibility of failure.

● **Does the state of the mouth generally justify the treatment?**
Another key question, especially when considering crowns, bridges or other advanced work. Does the periodontal and endodontic status preclude the placement of a crown or use of the tooth as an abutment? When considering a chrome denture or a bridge under the NHS you should be reasonably sure that there will be no need for further extractions in the arch.

NHS (General Dental Services Contracts) 2005 S1 P3 ¶21.

- **Is the proposed treatment cost-effective?**
  A difficult question this, but if you are going to have to spend more time, or more resources, but for little or no increased clinical gain, then the treatment is unlikely to be cost-effective and may be more suitable to be offered privately. There is a specific clause that restricts Providers from prescribing a denture or bridge whose cost or quantity is in excess of that which is reasonably necessary for the proper treatment of the patient.

- **Does the treatment need to be done in this course of treatment or should it be deferred?**
  There may be good reasons for deferring NHS treatments to a later course, for instance if you need to see whether preventive measures and advice you have given are improving their oral health. On the other hand, postponing part of a treatment in order to gain additional UDAs is 'gaming' and potentially in breach of your contract.

The Stable Table approach

Another approach is the so-called Stable Table. This model is intended to assist you in determining whether or not the treatment requested or required should be provided under NHS contract or outside the health service.

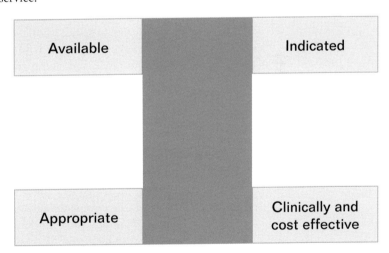

Figure 14: The 'Stable Table'.

Conceptually these blocks represent a table with four legs which have been laid out as though they were taken out of a flat-packed box. The intention is to gradually screw the legs of the table together and once all four legs are up, the table is a stable NHS platform from which NHS services can be served. If any of the four legs are missing, the table cannot be stable, and NHS provision would not be applicable.

● **Available**

Treatment can only be available to a particular patient if you have a contract to provide that service. For example, if you do not have a contract with the PCT to provide sedation or domiciliary services or advanced mandatory services then this will not be possible under the NHS. If the patient requires or requests these services you should offer them a referral under the NHS to another Provider. As an alternative you may offer these services under private contract. For example, a long-standing patient of the practice may be housebound and require domiciliary care. You could offer to refer the patient under the NHS, but the patient may wish to see you under private contract. This would be possible.

● **Indicated**

In providing treatment, certain options may be indicated for particular situations. For example, a root filled molar requiring cuspal coverage will need an onlay or crown; therefore, these are the only two types of restoration that are indicated for that particular patient for that particular purpose. There is no restriction on the material that can be used, as long as it secures oral health.

● **Clinically and cost effective**

A clinically effective intervention is one that does a patient more good than harm. A clinically effective treatment or intervention is effective in real-life circumstances, not just in ideal conditions.

A cost effective treatment is one that with regards to cost – which includes materials and labour costs – provides the longest lasting and most effective solution. In the example above, the most clinically effective solution could be an onlay and the most cost effective material to construct it could be cast-in alloys containing stainless steel or cobalt chromium or nickel chromium.

● **Appropriate**

This aspect tests the appropriateness of the particular intervention or treatment on the patient for whom this is intended. Specific clinical factors may determine the suitability or otherwise of a particular treatment. For example, a tooth that is being considered for a crown may lack sufficient bone support, may be periodontally compromised, may have a questionable endodontic status or occlusally insufficient clinical height. None of these may be absolute contraindications to the placement of a crown but may guide the clinician to either no treatment or different treatment. Thus, even if the other three legs of the stable table are constructed, that specific intervention or treatment may not be appropriate on the NHS. It may be possible to offer that treatment on a private basis but you must be mindful of the ethical dilemma and consent issues this raises: if it is not appropriate on the NHS it should not be clinically appropriate privately either, if you are acting in the patient's best interests. If the patient wants or demands the treatment then it could be made available to them as long as you obtain valid consent for the procedure. In such circumstances it is important to note down the discussion in the clinical records and invite the patient to sign a consent form. Dental Protection, together with Admor, have produced consent forms which are available as duplicate copies on the following subjects: minor oral surgery; tooth coloured restorations; endodontics; partial dentures.

An example

Using this stable table, the issue of posterior composites restorations being available on the NHS can be considered.

Once early carious lesions have penetrated into dentine they may well require intervention and restoration. Depending on the size of the lesion, composite restorations are often indicated for these single surface 2–4 mm depth lesions. They are effective and, for most patients, appropriate. They are also available on the NHS as composite resin is a material that is listed as appropriate for use in NHS patients. On the other hand, a patient who requests replacement of posterior amalgams with composites or merely wants carious cavities restored in composites for aesthetic purposes is not entitled to have these under NHS contract.

> **Treatment offered under the NHS should be necessary to improve oral health and should be long lasting. Treatment given for either cosmetic reasons, or reasons other than oral health improvement, should not be provided on the NHS.**

12 October 2005 (GR 5641).
Department of Health.

In the end it is down to your clinical judgement as to what is necessary to secure oral health and what is justifiable, but not necessary. Some examples of cases where you may want to mix NHS and private treatment include:

- Tooth whitening or the placing of a veneer to improve the patient's appearance are rarely, if ever, 'necessary' to improve their oral health, however important the patient feels it is to have them done. They are 'cosmetic' procedures, not 'necessary' and are not available under the GDS Contract.
- There are occasions, however, where one central incisor needs a crown but the other does not, although this might be needed some time in the future. You can crown the tooth that needs it under the NHS and the one that might need it later privately.
- You may feel that an acrylic denture is the necessary treatment to replace a missing tooth, but that you would like to offer the patient the opportunity to have a bridge.

The paperwork

Any proposals you may have for private treatment as an alternative to NHS care must be put on the treatment plan together with the cost to the patient. If the patient decides to accept the proposed private treatment then you must ensure that the patient signs the treatment plan in the appropriate place to indicate that they have understood and given informed consent.

It is also important to record in the clinical notes the different options made available to the patient, along with a note of the choice they made and why.

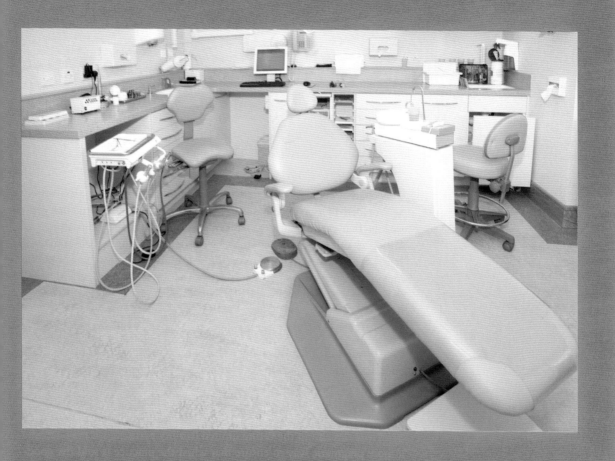

Part Three

RUNNING A PRACTICE

9 MANAGING ASSOCIATES

This chapter considers the new responsibilities faced by practice owners as Providers in a practice-based contract. It looks at the contractual obligations that create a legal responsibility to ensure that certain aspects of associates are checked, which may have implications for the self-employed status of associates. It also looks at some important clauses that should be included in any agreement that is made between associates and Providers, and proposes different models of paying associates.

New relationship

One of the fundamental changes that has occurred as result of the 2006 contract is the relationship between the practice owner and the associate. The practice owner is often a dentist who buys or sets up a practice either on their own or in partnership. That dentist may then buy further practices again on their own or with partners. Increasingly practices are owned by corporates and in the future limited liability partnerships may become a more pragmatic way to ensure that when the practice is sold the goodwill is retained as part of the sale.

The **Provider** – the person or partnership that holds a practice-based contract with the PCT – is responsible for the performance of the contract and with it the associates who are engaged or employed to perform dental services under the contract. This is akin to the relationship that existed between practice owners and assistants who worked on the practice owner's number. The practice owner would have to respond to any complaint or NHS disciplinary proceedings taken against the assistant.

In reality, the term 'associate' has no real meaning in the NHS any more and should be replaced with the term 'Performer', but for ease of use the terms will be interchangeable in this chapter.

In the 2006 contract there are several obligations on practice owners in relation to their associates which create a relationship very close to that of employer/employee, bringing with it the prospect of practice owners being vicariously liable for the actions of their associates. Registered healthcare professionals are personally responsible for their own professional acts and omissions of course, but whether they are true employees or working as self-employed independent Contractors, a practice owner might still be drawn into a legal action (such as a negligence claim) against a dentist who provided treatment at the practice. This is particularly likely to happen if the dentist has left the practice, leaving the practice owner or 'corporate' entity exposed as a more convenient and accessible target.

Before engaging a Performer the contract requires the Provider to take reasonable care to satisfy itself that the dentist is both suitably qualified and competent.

R NHS (General Dental Services Contracts) 2005 S3 P4 ¶27

In assessing competence the Provider is specifically directed to

- the person's qualifications
- their education and training
- their previous employment or work experience.

The contractual arrangements and statute regulations implicit in the engagement of associates make the link between Provider and associate closer than before and may make it impossible to avoid the practice owner being implicated and joined in any claim. It is important, therefore, that practice owners have appropriate indemnity cover; in that context 'occurrence-based' indemnity is the best.

New responsibilities

All dentist Performers in the practice, including associates and partners, need to be on a Performers List of a PCT. The Contractor must:

- ensure that the Performer is registered with the GDC and is on a dental Performers List
- ensure that, if the Performers are subject to any conditions applied by either the GDC or the PCT, they can comply with them
- check that the Performer has such clinical experience and training as are necessary to properly perform services under the contract
- check and be satisfied with two clinical references (see below)
- ensure that there are arrangements in place for the purpose of maintaining and updating the skills and knowledge of the Performer
- ensure that the dental practitioner participates in the appraisal system provided by the PCT.

These are in addition to all the terms of the contract which have to be complied with, such as the issue of treatment plans, involvement in the complaints procedures and being part of and involved in quality assurance and clinical governance. If Performers are not complying with the contract, the Providers will be held responsible by the PCT for rectifying this. This is particularly relevant with regards to the activity aspect of the contract and the provision of treatment. If a Performer is claiming treatment inappropriately or breaching the contract in some way, it will be the Provider who will be held accountable by the PCT.

References

The clinical references must relate to two recent posts (including any current post) which they held or are holding as dentists and which lasted for three months or more without a significant break. Where this is not possible, that person has to provide a full explanation and alternative referees.

This is over and above the checks that PCTs make when admitting a dentist onto a Performers List. In that case, GDC registration, membership of a defence organisation, two clinical references and Criminal Records Bureau (CRB) checks are done. It must be remembered, however, that those checks will be performed only once, as a dentist can be on a Performers List anywhere in the country. A practice owner has a very clear obligation to ensure that references apply to the most recent job.

There is no general or statutory obligation on an employer to give a reference for an ex-employee, but there may be a contractual obligation to do so. Associates may therefore want to create an obligation on the practice owner to ensure that a clinical reference is provided to them to enable them to take up a post elsewhere when they leave. The only way to do this is to ensure they sign an associate agreement with the practice.

If a practice owner does give a reference for an outgoing dentist they must take reasonable care to ensure that it is not misleading. If they deliberately or negligently mislead a potential new employer into thinking the dentist is better than they really are and the new employer can show they have suffered loss as a result of relying on the reference, the new employer can claim damages from the previous one. There is no obligation on the employer to make sure that the reference that has been given is fully comprehensive, just as long as it is not misleading.

Kidd v Axa Equity & Law Life Assurance Society plc and anon [2001] IRLR 301 High Court QB.

An important part of a vocational dental practitioner's application for a job as an associate at a new practice is a reference from their vocational trainer. It would be unfair to refuse a reference, but if asked about clinical skills of a former VDP about whom you had concerns, you might offer that their clinical skills are commensurate with the experience they have acquired.

There is most definitely an art to requesting and providing a reference to remain within the law. A proforma is a better way to request and provide a reference as it allows specific areas to be addressed. The proforma will include the details of the person giving the reference and their relationship to the candidate, including how closely they worked with them and for how long. A reference from a practice owner is likely to be considered preferable to one from a fellow associate, as the latter may not be in a position to give as comprehensive a reference as the former.

Points that could be included in this proforma may include:

● Do you have any concerns about the candidate's clinical abilities, including record keeping, history taking and making a good differential diagnosis?

● Please comment on the candidate's general attitude and conduct in relation to work.

● How many sick days have they had in the past 12 months?

● Please comment on communication skills and time management.

● Please provide any information about any previous or outstanding written complaints from patients, the PCT or other body including the GDC.

● What involvement has the candidate had in the running of the practice, involvement in setting up new systems and contributing to quality assurance and clinical governance initiatives?

● Would you employ this person again? Give your reasons why.

Accountability

While it is the Provider who enters into the contract with the PCT, the associates still have responsibilities. Firstly, they need to remain a Performer on the PCT's Performers List in order to continue providing NHS treatment. Secondly, they are personally involved in completing the FP17 claim forms manually or electronically: these carry their Performer number. In signing each treatment form or allowing their PIN number to be used for this purpose (which has the same legal effect as signing the form) they confirm their agreement to the various declarations on the form such as:

A whole new universe. *Risk Matters,* 11. Dental Protection Limited (www.dentalprotection.org).

> I have carried out all the care and treatment which the patient is willing to undergo that is currently necessary to secure oral health.
>
> I declare that I am properly entitled to practise under the current dental regulations and that the information I have given on this form is correct and complete. I understand that if it is not, appropriate action may be taken. For the purpose of verification of this and the prevention and detection of fraud and incorrectness, I consent to the disclosure of the relevant information from this form to and by the NHS Business Services Authority.

Performer notice period

Since the contractual relationship for the NHS contract is between the Provider and the PCT, the Performer has no notice period to comply with except that set out in their associate agreement with the Provider. This means the three months' notice required from a Provider terminating their NHS contract does not apply to a Performer leaving the practice. This in a sense is an internal matter for the Provider to arrange with their Performers.

Therefore, in order to protect the continuity of care for Providers and for associates to protect their income, it is important that a clause covering notice period is included. Three months is normal. There should also be provision for amending this notice period or doing away with it altogether with the consent of both parties. This ensures appropriate flexibility to cover most circumstances.

Any changes made to Performer personnel in the practice will need to be notified to the PCT in writing by the Provider.

Clause 229 Standard General Dental Services Contract

Employed or self-employed?

In a practice-based contract, where Providers are responsible for the Performers carrying out the contract, there are implications for the determination of self-employment of associates for tax purposes as well as employment legislation.

A dentist can work under a contract *of* service (employee) or under a contract *for* services (self-employed, independent contractor). There is no statutory definition of a contract of service or a contract for services. Indeed, what the parties call their relationship or what they consider it to be is not conclusive. It is the *reality* of the relationship that matters.

Employed or Self-employed. HM Revenue and Customs, www.hmrc.gov.uk/employment-status.

A combination of common law principles and precedent have determined what factors are relevant in deciding whether a person is employed or self-employed. There is no single test governing this question and all factors that are present in or absent from a particular case will be taken into consideration either by the HM Revenue and Customs or an Employment Tribunal who may be called upon in any case.

HMRC: formerly known as Inland Revenue.

In the list below, the more questions an associate can answer 'Yes' to, the more likely they are to be considered self-employed.

1) Do they set their own hours and decide what holidays to take, and when?
2) Do they risk their own money in the business?
3) Are they responsible for meeting any loss as well as taking any profit from the business?
4) Do they have to correct unsatisfactory work in their own time and their own expense?
5) Do they have a final say in how the business is run?
6) Can they hire someone to do the work or engage helpers at their own expense?

7) Do they provide the main items of equipment they need to do the job, not just the small tools or equipment that many employees provide for themselves?

As this list makes clear, many associates will fail the test, especially when answering questions 2, 3, 5 and 7. Conversely, answering 'Yes' to the following questions will probably mean the associate is an employee:

1) Do they have to do the work themselves?

2) Can someone tell them at any time what to do, where to carry out the work or when and how to do it?

3) Are they paid a salary?

4) Do they work fixed hours or a set number of hours every week or month?

5) Does the person they work for decide on the premises they work from?

The risk for the practice owner is that if the HMRC determines that the associate is an employee, they may be liable to pay Class 1 National Insurance contributions, and these could be backdated. The practice owner may also be liable for any damages awarded by an Employment Tribunal, for example, if an associate is claiming unfair dismissal and the Tribunal, using the tests above, determines that they are an employee.

For further information it is worth checking the HMRC website. A particularly useful tool is the Employment Status Indicator: the questions it asks provides the answers which help you to establish whether your position is an employed or self-employed one.

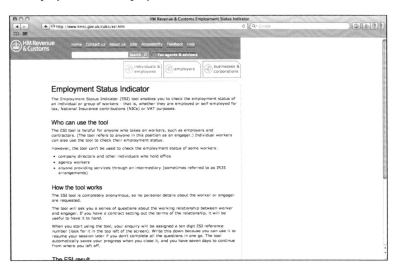

Figure 15: Employment Status Indicator on the HMRC website (www.hmrc.gov.uk/calcs/esi.htm).

Contractual terms

There are a number of associate agreements currently in circulation produced by membership organisations such as the British Dental Association and Confederation of Dental Employers as well as the corporates such as Oasis Dental Care Ltd, Rodericks, Integrated Dental Holdings and Optical Express. They vary in detail and complexity but all essentially try to ensure that the self-employed nature of the associate is paramount, while at the same time ensuring that the practice owner/Provider has sufficient control over the associate's UDA output as well as other issues relating to compliance with quality assurance and clinical governance protocols in the practice.

◗ Annex A to this chapter, p 106. The model of payment utilised by the practice to remunerate the associates will influence how the contract clauses are set out and the various rights the practice owner retains in withholding money if targets are not met.

Contracts should also ensure that overachievement of targets in a year are not paid or if they are there is an upper limit on each quarter. If a ceiling is not set for the maximum number of UDAs completed by an associate, the Contractor will exhaust their UDA quota before the year end and will therefore have to limit NHS service provision toward the end of the year.

Arrangements for terminating the contracts should be clear, and clauses protecting the goodwill of the practice should be included. This may include preventing outgoing dentists treating patients of the practice for a fixed time period or employing staff from the practice at any other location.

It is also worth considering how the practice will protect itself in the event of an investigation into the probity of NHS claims made by any outgoing Performers. This is particularly a problem if a commissioner seeks repayment for inappropriate/incorrect claims from a Provider when the claims relate to a Performer's activity. A clause in the associate agreement indemnifying the Provider against such recovery of funds should be considered.

The future of associate Performers

Since the new contract the number of associate positions have slowly contracted across England and Wales. This has been due to the loss of the natural organic growth that used to take place under the old contract, where practices would grow or new ones be established without the control of the PCT or the requirement to tender for UDAs as a prerequisite for growth. Associates now are not able simply to leave one practice and set up another; likewise, a practice cannot expand its capacity by adding a new surgery or extend its opening hours and start treating more NHS patients without allocated funding from the NHS.

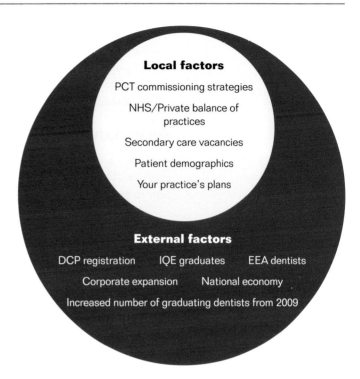

Local factors

PCT commissioning strategies

NHS/Private balance of practices

Secondary care vacancies

Patient demographics

Your practice's plans

External factors

DCP registration   IQE graduates   EEA dentists

Corporate expansion   National economy

Increased number of graduating dentists from 2009

Figure 16: Factors affecting the job market.

The local health economy has an increasing impact on the dental workforce. Commissioning decisions will influence the growth or decline of certain practices, depending on local priorities and targets, as will the decision to establish new practices.

⬦ p 42. Young dentists completing vocational training are often not able to stay on in their practices as funding is not always guaranteed. The blueprint for many commissioners is to concentrate their efforts on developing larger practices, with training capabilities for all the team. Therefore these practices may be appointed on a long-term basis as stable training practices. One of the added benefits for a PCT hosting a Deanery-approved vocational training post is the VDP's service provision. This represents at least 1,875 UDAs at no further cost to the PCT. More enlightened PCTs are being proactive in supporting practices through the VT application process where oral health needs or access demand it.

The type of associate a practice needs is changing. Although there is a clear requirement for UDAs to be completed, as the contract shifts its emphasis to quality, associates will need to become an integral part of the quality agenda with its attendant demonstration of compliance.

Practices will be looking for the following features in associates:

- ethical and hard working
- team players
- possessing management skills
- possessing communication skills

- committed to practice
- potential partnership material
- possessing skills and demonstrable ability to develop private practice
- flexible.

Associate payment models

There are a number of different ways of paying associates in the new contract. There are two important points to remember when deciding how to pay an associate:

- There should be some link between pay and UDA activity or alternatively clauses in the contract allowing over or under payment to be corrected.
- Since the contract value is fixed, any payment system must take into consideration variable costs, such as laboratory bills, that will be incurred by associates.
- The Provider should pay the Performer in the same way they are paid by the Commissioner. As the contract starts to rely less on UDA activity in the future and more on quality and capitation/ registered patient numbers, the Provider will have to build this in to ensure that they do not have to seek recovery of payments from Performers in the event that targets are not met and commissioners claw back money.

There is no one method of payment that suits all practices: this is why the different associate payment models have been set out in Annex A below. Ultimately it is for the practice owner to discuss the remuneration model in an open and professional manner with your associates. It is not always about deriving the most profit out of the system: a happy, contented team is likely to deliver better care to the patients and more loyalty to the practice. As the NHS contracting models change to incorporate the quality criteria and numbers of patient treated these models will need to change. Annex B quotes from the BDA Practice Owner/Associate Code of Conduct (reprinted with kind permission).

- These associate payments models are all based on an assumption that 50 per cent of the Performer's contract value covers the expenses associated with operating the practice in relation to that particular Performer. This 50 per cent deduction has its basis in historical custom and practice (by which is meant a particular practice has been operating in a workplace so regularly that everyone takes it as read that it will always apply). The superannuation calculations for Performers are based on applying a percentage to the gross contract value that has been assigned because an assumption is made about the amount of the practice expenses ratio.

- In the near term, the percentage model is likely to continue to exist because it is familiar. However, new models will need to evolve to reflect the fundamental changes in the 2006 contract and the 'return on investment' concept is just one possible step in that direction. To assign average percentage ratios to all Performers irrespective of their efficiency is itself flawed, as the more efficient will be subsiding less efficient Performers. Any evolution should take into account the segregation of fixed costs from the contract value and demand an equal contribution from all Performers pro-rata to their consumption of those resources and some form of direct allocation of actual variable expenses per individual Performer – those that incur more will pay more in this way.

- As dentists get to grips with the business challenges of the GDS Contract, contract values are tempered with growth monies or by the PCTs re-allocating surplus funds (up to 31 March 2011 at least) at UDA values that may differ from those allocated to the practice at the outset. Providers will need to introduce more elegant and appropriate methods of Performer remuneration – ones that reflect future trends rather than replicate an older mindset.

- One of these models will be to pay associate Performers a flat UDA value that is not subject to a 50 per cent deduction. This may be amended to make the associate entirely responsible for the cost of their lab work. It is anomalous that the practice owner pays a proportion of the laboratory bill for a crown or denture when they have no influence on the treatment planning decision, its execution or, in many cases, where the work is sent to be completed. As these are entirely based on the associate's clinical decision, it seems logical that it is they who should be financially responsible for that decision.

- The likely change to a contract model, split into three components, will compound the problems for Providers to ensure that a fair and equitable system of payment is established that both rewards and incentivises the Performer but at the same time ensures that they deliver what the commissioner wants from the Provider.

- The three components – activity (UDAs), quality and continuing care type registration payments (based on numbers of patients treated) – will be measured in different ways. A Performer not delivering the quality criteria set out by commissioners, for example, may have an impact on the practices' funding and therefore the associate agreement. Any associate payment model should reflect this risk accordingly.

Model 1: 12 equal instalments

In this model the contract value agreed with the Performers is divided into 12 equal portions and this becomes the gross fee that is paid to the Performer according to the formula below:

> **Annual Contract Value (ACV) divided by 12 plus private fees =**
> **Gross for the month [G]**
>
> **Then**
>
> **[G] minus lab fees = Actual gross [AG]**

The associate is then paid [AG] divided by 50 per cent minus the NHS superannuation allocation.

The superannuation deductions will have been calculated based on the Annual Contract Value and will be made on a monthly basis by Dental Services automatically from information provided by the PCT.

Advantages

- It is familiar to most dentists since that is roughly how the majority of associates have been paid in this country for many years.
- It is likely to be favoured by Performers as it seems to be fair and equitable. (For an associate with a low Annual Contract Value who wants to increase his output, however, this model is quite restrictive.)

Disadvantages

- Simple as this model is, it is not related to performance. This means that if an associate does not achieve their UDA targets the Provider will have to claw the money back.
- There may be tax implications as the NHS sum will be fixed each month which makes it hard to resist the claim that this amounts to a fixed NHS salary and therefore using this model means that employment law rights accrue to the dentist as well as PAYE tax liabilities.
- This model is not an ideal way to work in the new era.

Model 2: Payment by individual UDA

In this model, a monetary value for each UDA in pounds is calculated for each individual associate based on their historical earnings during the test period and becomes the basis of payment. The UDA therefore becomes a form of currency and is the basis of the gross payment as follows:

> **Annual Contract Value (ACV) for individual associate divided by UDA target allocated to individual associate = UDA value (UV)**
>
> **UV multiplied by UDAs achieved for that month by associate plus private fees = Gross for the month [G]**
>
> **Then**
>
> **[G] minus lab fees = Actual gross [AG]**

The associate is then paid [AG] divided by 50 per cent minus the NHS superannuation allocation.

The superannuation deductions will have been calculated based on the Annual Contract Value and will be made on a monthly basis by Dental Services automatically from information provided by the PCT. In this model and in models 3–5 the NHS fee paid to the associate will vary each month. This means that a superannuation calculation based on the correct amount of total contract value paid to the individual associate will need to be made at the end of the financial year to ensure that the correct amount is deducted. This is particularly important if the associate fails to achieve their allocated UDA targets since on this payment system they will end up paying more in NHS superannuation contributions.

The following controls need to be applied in this model by the Provider.

- Laboratory fees

  This system allows the associate to achieve their UDAs in any way they wish but there is an incentive to deliver 'quick' UDAs via laboratory based items since 12 points can be achieved sometimes more rapidly than check-ups and restorative based items such as molar endodontics.

  Laboratory costs are not directly remunerated in this system as they are in a fee for item system and they therefore become a cost centre to the Provider if the Provider is paying 50 per cent of the associate's laboratory bill.

  First set a laboratory budget for each individual associate based on their historical test period activity. The associate should endeavour to stay within their set laboratory budget on a quarterly basis which would mean creating a waiting list for laboratory based treatments if a budget is exceeded. If they exceed their laboratory fee budget, they would either pay for the laboratory bill themselves with no contribution from the Provider or with a reduced contribution, say 15 per cent.

  The budgets should be set with some elasticity to take into account changing practice demographics, especially if new patients are being seen by a particular associates, as well as seasonal variation and other variables that may not be in the practice's control. Performers should be allowed clinical freedom to treat patients on the NHS according to need without too many restrictions, but budgetary and fiscal discipline need to be exercised.

● Ceiling on individual earnings

Since the associate is being paid on each UDA they achieve, and there is only a fixed number of UDAs in the practice pot it is important that each associate is allocated a fixed number of UDAs above which they earn no more.

This allocation should be notionally divided up over the year on a monthly or quarterly basis to ensure that NHS activity is provided by each associate evenly across the year. This will ensure there is no shortage of UDAs at the end of the year or shortfall in achieving UDA targets which would require a disproportionate amount of activity to complete.

It is important that measuring tools are established by the Provider to ensure that UDA activity for each associate is monitored on a monthly basis and Key Performance Indicators (KPIs) are recorded. The value of some of this information being captured automatically by computer software programmes cannot be overemphasised.

Some KPIs worth measuring are:

- associates' UDAs completed
- associates' PCR (Patient Charge Revenue) – this is something the PCT will be measuring on a practice basis and there may be a contractual requirement for the practice to achieve a certain annual target (if you divide the PCR collected per month by the number of UDAs completed you will get a ratio that demonstrates how much PCR is collected for every UDA earned)
- associates' private fees
- materials spend as a percentage of gross fees
- NHS laboratory fees as a percentage of Annual Contract Value
- number of new patients (NHS and private)
- number of patient complaints
- waiting time for next 30 minute appointment.

Advantages

- There is a clear link between payment and performance and the model maintains an incentive for associates to achieve targets set for them. Since there is a link between performance and pay this may improve the chances of resisting a claim by the Inland Revenue that the associate is being paid a salary.

Disadvantages

- It is output driven with very little consideration given to quality. Unfortunately it could be argued that the whole system of UDAs does not reward quality and this payment model merely reflects this.

Model 3: Per practice UDA value

This is similar to Model 2. However, in this model, instead of the UDA value being calculated for each individual associate, an average value for the practice is calculated so that each associate is paid at the same rate.

> **Practice Annual Contract Value (PACV) for the whole practice divided by the total annual number of UDAs the practice has to achieve = Practice UDA value (PUV)**
>
> **PUV multiplied by UDAs achieved for that month by that associate plus private fees = Gross for the month [G]**
>
> **Then**
>
> **[G] minus lab fees = Actual gross [AG]**

The associate is then paid [AG] divided by 50 per cent minus the NHS superannuation allocation.

By averaging out the UDA value across the practice, some will benefit but other associates will find their UDA value dragged down. In their case the reason why they have achieved a high UDA value is because they were efficient in the old system. If they maintain their efficiency under the new contract the benefit to them is that they will achieve their UDA targets and release a more valuable commodity – time. This can be utilised to do more private work, or for continuing professional development or leisure pursuits.

Advantages

- This model has the same advantages as Model 2 but has the added advantage that it is simpler to administer since each associate is being paid at the same UDA rate.

- It is also easier to administer any internal adjustments where a dentist does NHS work on a patient for another dentist and the claim form is sent off in the absent dentist's name. This is applicable if a dentist is off sick or has left the practice without completing a course of treatment on a particular patient. (However, with the inherent difficulties in making these adjustments internally between dentists, especially where several items of treatment are carried out in the same charge band, it is better for a patient to start and complete a course of treatment with the same dentist.)

Disadvantages

- It disadvantages high value associates. (Each associate will have a different UDA value based on their test period activity, This range could vary by as much as £10–15 between associates, especially if you compare a part-time practitioner seeing a regular stable patient base that require only maintenance care with a full-time associate seeing all the new patients who have high treatment needs.)

Model 4: Per practice UDA value less return on investment

In this model, the practice owner takes a percentage of the practice Annual Contract Value at the start of the year as a guaranteed baseline payment to cover their return on investment (ROI).

ROI is a well recognised business principle. It is the financial benefit derived from the investment made and is expressed as a percentage of a specific investment. In business terms it is a measure of the profitability of a particular investment.

A practice owner will have made a significant investment in the practice both in terms of time and finance with no guaranteed return on that investment at any time other than when the practice is sold. This model allows the practice owner to achieve that return on the NHS side of the business each year, and they may decide to reinvest some or all of it back into the practice, for example, to upgrade the practice facilities.

The perception from associates can be that the practice owner is somehow being greedy or that the UDA values are being reduced to increase the practice owner's profits. The reality, of course, is that the dental practice is a business and the practice owner is entitled to a return on that risk.

Figures from industry professionals and banking suggest that a 10 per cent ROI is reasonable for a dental practice. On that basis the following calculations apply which are exactly the same as Model 3 except that the UDA value is reduced by 10 per cent.

> **Practice Annual Contract Value (PACV) for the whole practice multiplied by 0.9 and divided by the total annual number of UDAs the practice has to achieve = Practice UDA value (PUV)**
>
> **PUV multiplied by UDAs achieved for that month by that associate plus private fees = Gross for the month [G]**
>
> **Then**
>
> **[G] minus lab fees = Actual gross [AG]**

The associate is then paid [AG] divided by 50 per cent minus the NHS superannuation allocation.

This has the same effect as reducing the percentage paid to the perfomer by 5 per cent. Some practice owners have offset this reduction in NHS percentage to the associates by increasing the percentage paid for private fees by 5 per cent.

Model 5: Per practice UDA less ROI with pooled activity

This is the same model as above with the single exception that, rather than have each Performer given an individual annual ceiling on UDAs that they have to achieve, the entire practice's UDAs are pooled as a single resource. The Performers will then work at whatever pace they feel comfortable and are paid on a monthly basis on the UDAs they achieved for that month.

This can of course amount to a free-for-all, with competition between associates to see as many patients as possible to earn their living. It can also mean that the practice UDA allocation is exhausted well before the end of the financial year. This may disadvantage regular NHS practice patients, as there may be no NHS activity remaining in the practice to treat them.

Some practice owners have adopted this system with some modifications such as an upper quarterly limit on the number of UDAs that are pooled so that when the UDAs are utilised, the next quota of UDAs are not released into the system until the start of the next quarter. Other controls include a minimum allocation to associates, especially part timers or those practitioners who are slower or doing more complex, time-consuming treatment such as endodontics on behalf of others in the practice.

The same formula as Model 4 applies, therefore:

> **Practice Annual Contract Value (PACV) for the whole practice multiplied by 0.9 and divided by the total annual number of UDAs the practice has to achieve = Practice UDA value (PUV)**
>
> **PUV multiplied by UDAs achieved for that month by that associate plus private fees = Gross for the month [G]**
>
> **Then**
>
> **[G] minus lab fees = Actual gross [AG]**

The associate is then paid [AG] divided by 50 per cent minus the NHS superannuation allocation.

ANNEX B
BDA Practice Owner/Associate Code of Conduct

Associates and practice owners will:

- deal openly and honestly with each other
- provide each other with clear and transparent information
- deal promptly and openly with problems and disagreements that arise
- seek the help of the BDA in resolving disputes.

An associate expects their practice owner to:

- provide a reasonable and fair written agreement with time to consider the terms before signing
- provide a copy of the signed, written agreement
- provide a copy of their monthly NHS Schedule/Performer Statement and a monthly summary of private patient fees earned
- provide sufficient patients to obtain their expected level of earnings and performance targets
- agree with the associate reasonable appointment times
- agree performance targets that are reasonable and achievable in the circumstances of the practice
- not penalise the associate financially if targets cannot be met for reasons that are the responsibility of the practice owner
- provide opportunities to increase their professional experience and clinical skills if they wish
- provide the services of a suitably experienced and trained dental nurse
- provide a reasonable period of maternity/paternity/adoption leave
- pay the full amount of any NHS maternity, sickness, paternity, adoption and commitment payments to which they are entitled
- keep the associate informed of practice changes, particularly if the practice is to be sold
- ensure that the associate's NHS claims are completed accurately and submitted promptly
- enable the associate to use the services of a dental laboratory of their choice and agree with the associate the dental materials to be used
- provide a surgery that is fit for purpose and ensure that any breakdowns are rectified quickly
- provide protected time to ensure that their knowledge and skills are up to date
- give a reasonable period of notice of termination of their contract and enable reasonable arrangements to be made for their departure from the practice, including the information that is to be given to the patient
- enable the associate to be an integral part of the practice team
- provide a copy of any NHS contract to which the practice is party.

The practice owner expects that their associates will:

- provide a high standard of clinical care to their patients
- comply with reasonable practice rules and procedures
- work as part of the practice team and treat members of the practice team with courtesy and respect
- use the surgery time that is made available to them for the treatment of practice patients
- make every effort to meet agreed performance targets
- pay a reasonable amount for their licence to practise at the practice
- comply with any contract that the practice has with the NHS
- when leaving the practice, complete treatment commenced
- take responsibility for work that needs to be replaced or repaired
- keep full and accurate records of clinical work maintain high professional standards
- adopt high standards of customer service
- give reasonable notice of their intention to take holidays or study leave.

Patients expect:

- practice owners and associates to work together as part of the practice team
- practice owners to ensure that they work with associates who provide a good standard of clinical care
- associates and practice owners to cover for each other in the case of illness or holidays
- associates and practice owners to share information where this is in the best interests of patients
- not to be involved in disputes between associates and practice owners
- to be advised when an associate is leaving the practice and to be told, if they ask, where the associate is now practising.

10 CONTRACT VALUE

Annual Contract Value applies to a GDS Contract. PDS Agreements have an Annual Agreement Value; however the principles are the same for both. 'Annual Contract Value' will be used for both types in this chapter.

This chapter looks at the Annual Contract Value, how it is calculated and applied in the practice. The new concept of a 'blended contract' is also described. Finally, additional payments to individual dentists are considered, although details of who is eligible and how to claim them are beyond the scope of this book.

Annual Contract Value

Based on a combination of the pre-contract test period earnings and any changes to include growth money and the annual increase determined by the Secretary of State, there is an agreed Annual Contract Value. This is paid, less any amounts collected by the practice in patients' charges, in twelve equal monthly instalments on the first working day of the month, by the Dental Services section of the NHS Business Services Authority (BSA).

Payments made by PCTs to dentists under a GDS Contract are laid down in directions by the Secretary of State in a Statement of Financial Entitlements (SFE). The PCT has to make these payments and has no discretion in doing this. The PCT are responsible for entering the amounts to be paid using the Payments-on-Line system as well as any variations during the year.

Some new acronyms have been introduced:

There is also a Baseline Number of Units of Orthodontic Activity (BNUOA).

- Baseline Number of Units of Dental Activity (BNUDA) – the number to units of dental activity you will agree to provide
- Monthly Annual Contact Value Payments (Monthly ACVPs) – the gross amount you will be paid each month
- Negotiated Annual Contract Value (NACV) – from 2009 all contracts will be the subject of negotiation
- Annual Domiciliary and Sedation Services Payments (ADSSP) – payments in relation to the provision of these additional services.

Negotiated Annual Contract Value

The Negotiated Annual Contract Value applies if you were providing general dental services on 31 March 2009. It is based on your gross earnings from fees and allowances during the financial year 2008–9 and will be the contract value negotiated with the PCT based on previous activity and future projections and plans.

Your GDS Contract will specify the number of units of dental activity or units of orthodontic activity you are to provide.

The Statement of Financial Entitlements makes provision in Section 2.4 for an Annual Contract Value adjustment at the start of each financial year. This is determined by the Secretary of State following advice given by the Doctors and Dentists Review Body (DDRB), an independent advisory body appointed in July 1971. The DDRB takes evidence from the Department of Health and professional representatives such as the British Dental Association, British Orthodontic Society and the Dental Practitioners Association. They then make separate proposals to the Governments in England, Wales, Scotland and Northern Ireland which may choose to accept the recommendations in part or in full.

Dental Services will automatically add this onto each monthly payment to the Contractor. The intention is to reflect rising prices, cost of materials and salaries, recruitment and retention of professional staff and other market specific conditions.

Should the annual increase be passed to Performers?

In the old contract the annual fee increase was effectively added to each item of treatment. This meant that it translated into a fee increase for the associate through activity. In the 2006 contract the gross fee increase is added to the Annual Contract Value paid to the Provider, so that there is no direct method of passing it to the associate through activity other than via an uplift in the UDA value paid to each Performer.

There is no guidance from the Department of Health as to how Performers should be paid. The British Dental Association is silent on the issue: they recognise that this is a decision for practice owners to make, depending on their own circumstances and arrangements.

Practice owners need to be open and fair in their dealings with professional colleagues. If they decide not to pass on the annual increase, practice owners should give some justification for their decisions based on any practice plans for investments they have or will make in the coming financial year. They may consider improving other terms and conditions to compensate for this such as holiday, CPD time or percentage split of private income.

If the annual fee increase is never passed to the Performer the real value of the NHS component of their income will depreciate over time. This may be acceptable only if their relative private incomes are increasing or changes to the practice are made to improving working lives. Practice owners may wish to consider utilising the fee increase due to each Performer as an incentive to comply with clinical governance requirements.

Monthly Contract Payments

The Annual Contract Value Payment (ACVP) is paid in 12 instalments, less the patients' charges collected. These payments are referred to as the monthly contract payment and are paid on the first working day of the month.

Once a treatment for each patient is completed, you send the NHS DPD an FP17 (on paper or electronically via EDI link) which will indicate the complexity of the course of treatment (by reference to its banding), whether the patient pays charges or is exempt.

Using this data the amount of NHS charges that should have been collected will be calculated and deducted from the monthly contract payment. This calculation will be made on your 'scheduling date' as under the old GDS, but instead of receiving the money straight away on that date, you will receive it on the first working day of the following month.

Every month the Provider is sent a pay statement and each Performer receives a copy of their monthly superannuation allocation and a summary of the forms processed.

Guide to Monthly Pay Statements
NHS BSA (www.nhsbsa.nhs.uk)

The Provider pay schedule shows:

- your Actual Annual Contract Value and the monthly contract payment, prior to any deductions
- the amount of the NHS charges that should have been collected and any other deductions that need to be made, for example, for any previous overpayment and for your superannuation
- the amount of the monthly contract payment following these deductions
- any other payments, such as seniority payments which will include the name of the dentist who should receive it
- net superannuable pay in respect of each dentist in the practice
- the number of UDAs or UOAs the dentist is contracted to provide during the year and running totals of how many have been provided and how many are left to be provided.

Pension contributions

PCTs will continue to be responsible for paying the 'employer's' superannuation contributions for dentists who are members of the scheme. The use of the word 'employer' here does not mean you are employed by them, however. They are also responsible for forwarding your contribution to the NHS Pensions Agency, and this amount is deducted from your monthly payment. These deductions will be based on a reasonable estimate of what each Performer's gross earnings will be.

At the end of the financial year, a reconciliation will take place and you may be asked to pay any shortfall or receive a repayment. Depending on the way in which associate Performers are paid, this will need to be done if individual Performers' targets set at the start of the year are not achieved and UDAs are reallocated to other Performers.

Payments for domiciliary and sedation services

If you agree to provide sedation services or domiciliary services under your GDS Contract you must agree with your PCT the number of such courses of treatment that you will provide each year and how much you will be paid. This Annual Domiciliary and Sedation Services Payment will also be paid in monthly instalments. It will also be uprated annually.

The 'blended' contract

See Chapter 2, 'Setting the Scene', p 15.

The first contracts were mostly a fixed payment for a fixed number of UDAs (or UOAs). In March 2010 the Department of Health announced that, following the Steele Review, some 'blended' contracts would be trialled, with

> **dentists being directly rewarded for the number of patients seen, the level of treatment each patient receives and the quality of that care.**

Note that quality of care is expressed in terms of Key Performance Indicators.

In the future registration payments might also be included. Although this appears to be a radical departure from the original contract, the principles remain the same: an Annual Contract Value (divided into 12 monthly payments) is paid for an agreed level of service. What changes with the blended contract is that the level of service is divided into a number of elements; in most cases these are in addition to the number of UDAS required, which remains the same. Allocating money within the practice is likely to be more complex and is an important factor to be considered.

Additional payments to individual dentists

Seniority payments

Seniority payments will continue to be made if you reached the age of 55 before March 2008. You will need to apply in writing to your PCT for these to be paid. You will be entitled to a Monthly Seniority Payment of 21.72 per cent of your net monthly pensionable earnings; the maximum amount payable in respect of any month is £604.44.

Vocational Training payments

If you have vocational trainee in your practice, you will receive four different payments:

- a training grant, to go to the trainer
- reimbursement of the trainee's salary
- reimbursement of the employer's national insurance contributions
- the service cost of employing the trainee.

The funding for vocational training does not come from the PCT, so if you want to keep the VDP on as an associate after the VT year, this will need the consent of the PCT as they will have to provide the funding. This may not always be forthcoming.

This has a potentially significant impact on the employment market since VDPs have to find a job elsewhere if no longer able to stay at their training practice, either because there is no funding or because the trainer is appointed for a three-year period and has to take on another VDP. Depending on funding and PCTs' commissioning strategies the new associate Performer may have difficulty finding another job in the NHS.

Payments for maternity, paternity and adoption leave

Your employees have rights to time off for ante-natal care, maternity leave, paternity leave, adoption leave and parental leave under employment legislation. Dentists working in your practice may also be entitled to payments from the PCT in respect of a period of maternity leave, paternity leave or adoption leave. You will need to study the Regulations to check entitlement, the amounts payable and how to apply.

Payments for long-term sickness absence

Dentists working in your practice may be entitled to payments from the PCT in respect of a period of long-term sickness absence. They are not payable for the first four weeks of absence, nor for more than 22 weeks. You will need to study the Regulations to check entitlement, the amounts payable and how to apply.

Reimbursement of non-domestic rates

You may be able to claim reimbursement of the non-domestic rates payable in relation to any premises at which you provide NHS services. There are regulations relating to this entitlement and only a proportion may be paid if your practice's total earnings are less than 90 per cent from the NHS.

Capital payments

Capital payments, such as they are, are included within the Annual Contract Value. However, under Section 180 of the Health and Social Care Act, a PCT may provide assistance or support to those providing, or proposing to provide both primary medical services and primary dental services contract. It adds that 'assistance' includes 'financial assistance.' During 2005/06 all such development money was targeted towards primary medical services, but from 2006/07 primary dental services are also supposed to be included in the distribution of capital funding, the allocation of which is a responsibility of the Strategic Health Authority.

Guide to your monthly pay schedule

Here is some guidance to assist you in interpreting your monthly pay schedule.

- Each provider will receive a summary of forms, a provider's summary and a pay statement.
- Each performer will receive a monthly superannuation notification.

Don't forget that although payments are made on the first working day of each month your forms will still be processed in accordance with the date specified in the scheduling programme. A copy of the scheduling programme can be found on the dentist information pack page of the DPD's website, www.dpb.nhs.uk The page can be accessed from the Dentist homepage.

The number of forms submitted in each band and number of associated UDAs

Breakdown of charge exempt courses by category

Breakdown of orthodontic courses of treatment by category

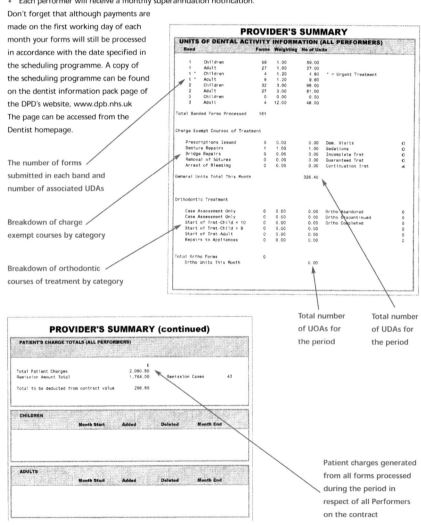

Total number of UOAs for the period

Total number of UDAs for the period

Patient charges generated from all forms processed during the period in respect of all Performers on the contract

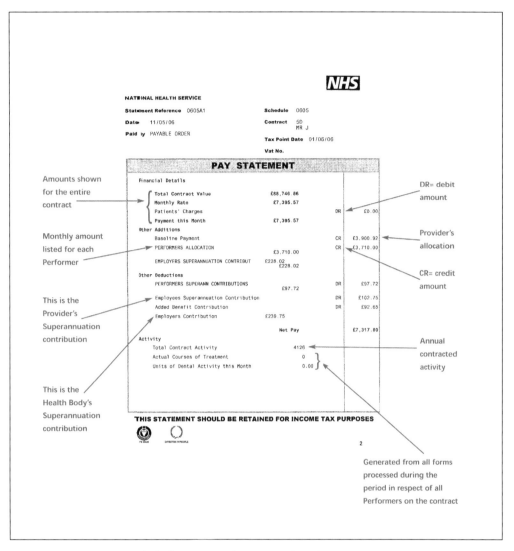

Left: Guide to monthly pay schedules Part 1, p 22.

Above: Guide to monthly pay schedules Part 1, p 23.

Provider pay statement

There may be occasions where the provider receives more than one copy of the pay statement. The example we have used below is one where two pay statements have been generated.

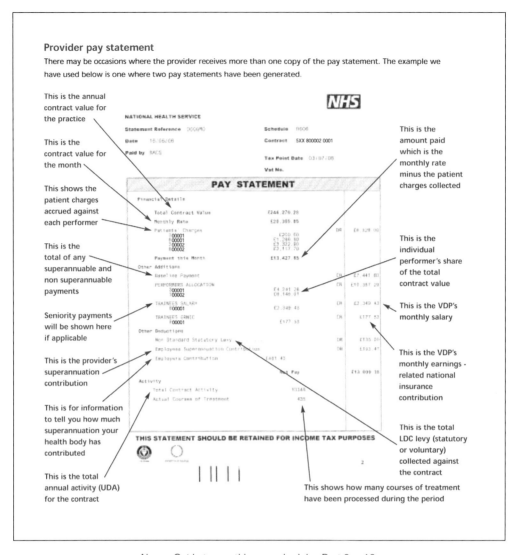

This is the annual contract value for the practice

This is the contract value for the month

This shows the patient charges accrued against each performer

This is the total of any superannuable and non superannuable payments

Seniority payments will be shown here if applicable

This is the provider's superannuation contribution

This is for information to tell you how much superannuation your health body has contributed

This is the total annual activity (UDA) for the contract

This is the amount paid which is the monthly rate minus the patient charges collected

This is the individual performer's share of the total contract value

This is the VDP's monthly salary

This is the VDP's monthly earnings - related national insurance contribution

This is the total LDC levy (statutory or voluntary) collected against the contract

This shows how many courses of treatment have been processed during the period

Above: Guide to monthly pay schedules Part 2, p 13.

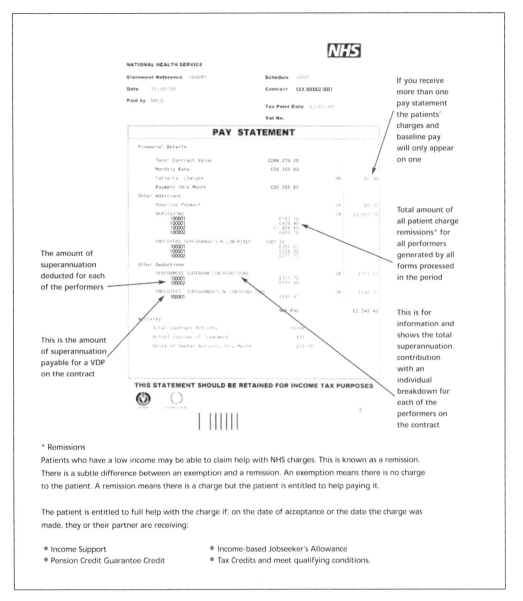

The amount of superannuation deducted for each of the performers

This is the amount of superannuation payable for a VDP on the contract

If you receive more than one pay statement the patients' charges and baseline pay will only appear on one

Total amount of all patient charge remissions* for all performers generated by all forms processed in the period

This is for information and shows the total superannuation contribution with an individual breakdown for each of the performers on the contract

* Remissions

Patients who have a low income may be able to claim help with NHS charges. This is known as a remission. There is a subtle difference between an exemption and a remission. An exemption means there is no charge to the patient. A remission means there is a charge but the patient is entitled to help paying it.

The patient is entitled to full help with the charge if, on the date of acceptance or the date the charge was made, they or their partner are receiving:

- Income Support
- Pension Credit Guarantee Credit
- Income-based Jobseeker's Allowance
- Tax Credits and meet qualifying conditions.

Above: Guide to monthly pay schedules Part 2, p 15.

Monthly superannuation notification

Each performer will receive a copy of the monthly superannuation notification.

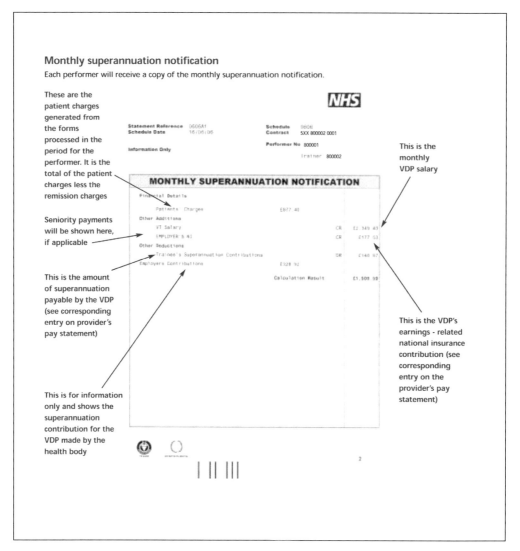

These are the patient charges generated from the forms processed in the period for the performer. It is the total of the patient charges less the remission charges

Seniority payments will be shown here, if applicable

This is the amount of superannuation payable by the VDP (see corresponding entry on provider's pay statement)

This is for information only and shows the superannuation contribution for the VDP made by the health body

This is the monthly VDP salary

This is the VDP's earnings - related national insurance contribution (see corresponding entry on the provider's pay statement)

Above: Guide to monthly pay schedules Part 2, p 16.

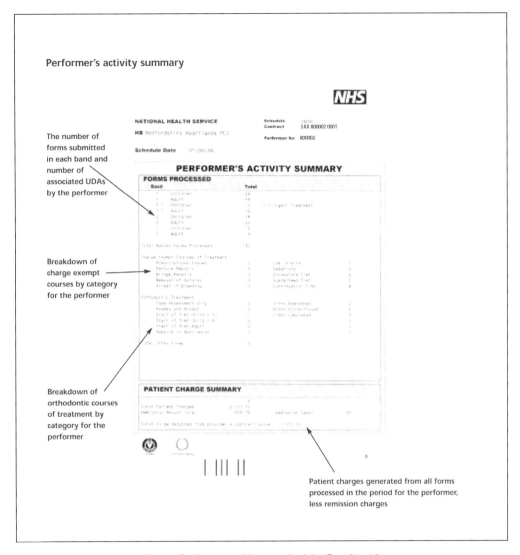

The number of forms submitted in each band and number of associated UDAs by the performer

Breakdown of charge exempt courses by category for the performer

Breakdown of orthodontic courses of treatment by category for the performer

Patient charges generated from all forms processed in the period for the performer, less remission charges

Above: Guide to monthly pay schedules Part 2, p 18.

Reproduced with kind permission of NHSBSA and available on their website:
www.nhsbsa.nhs.uk/DentalServices/861.aspx

11 MONITORING YOUR CONTRACT

This chapter describes the principles of performance management as well as how your contract will be monitored both by your PCT and the BDA's Dental Services. It includes consideration of the UDA as a measure of output as well as the widely used monitoring toolkit. Finally, it looks at how you can use 'capacity planning' to ensure you achieve your UDA targets.

Performance management

Performance management, Successful Delivery Toolkit, Office of Government Commerce. www.ogc.gov.uk/sdtoolkit.

Performance management is the activity of tracking performance against targets and identifying opportunities for improvement – but not just looking back at past performance. The focus of performance management is the future – what do you need to be able to do and how can you do things better?

Managing performance both from the practice's own point of view as well as the PCT's perspective is about managing for results, which in simple terms means focusing on the outputs of the processes and activities undertaken by the practice at varying levels.

Performance-based management at any level in an organisation should demonstrate that:

- you know what you are aiming for
- you know what you have to do to meet your objectives
- you know how to measure progress towards your objectives
- you can detect performance problems and remedy them.

The importance of understanding how performance management works cannot be emphasised too much: without these measures a practice becomes a rudderless organisation, buffeted by any winds of change with no control over its direction nor with any means of charting its position relative to its own abilities or that of other practices.

There are a number of business tools that can be utilised to track performance, one of which is the Balanced Score card. This has been adapted for use in many industries in order to translate a practice's vision and strat-

▶ Chapter 16, 'Business considerations', p 214.

egy into action and has now been harnessed by the NHS for monitoring dental practice performance.

In primary dental care there are a number of performance measures against which dentists are judged, either actively – for example, BSA Dental Services information on treatment patterns, unique patients seen in a 24-month period or banding profiles – or passively, such as the GDC *Standards for Dental Professionals*.

Published by GDC (May 2005) and available from the GDC website: www.gdc-uk.org.

Dental practices need to understand how performance management works in the NHS and to integrate the processes and measures so that they are able to respond quickly to any changes required of them. The NHS is in constant flux but the demands from it will be two-fold:

- to deliver high-quality services that meet the needs of patients and stakeholders (such as the PCT)
- to do this within the constraints of available resources.

Information technology is at the heart of a practice's ability to measure and manage itself and removes the reliance on information provided to it by third parties such as the BSA or the PCT. Being able to generate your own reliable data – in real time – puts you in a better position to gauge your practice's own performance at any given time and allows you to challenge third party data at, for example, mid-year reviews. It is in fact implicit that the practice itself should provide its own data if it needs to justify any shortfall in activity.

> Where a mid-year review is required by the Primary Care Trust […] the PCT and the Contractor shall discuss at the review –
> (a) any written evidence the Contractor puts forward to demonstrate that it has performed a greater number of units of dental activity or units of orthodontic activity during the first half of the financial year than those notified to it
> (b) any reasons that the Contractor puts forward for the level of activity in the first half of the financial year.

Ⓡ NHS (General Dental Services Contracts) 2006 P6 S3 P8 ¶58 (6).

Practices need to measure and manage organisational performance in order to understand how well they are performing against their own strategic goals and objectives. These goals may be allied to increasing the value of private income in the practice or changing the focus of delivery of NHS care. It is beyond the scope of this text to cover how goals and objectives are set by organisations but it is important that practices have a clear direction of where they are going.

Performance management in a practice involves managing resources such as clinical and non-clinical staff as well as the processes of delivering dentistry. Performance measures need to be:

- **Directional** – to confirm that you are on track to reach the goals.
- **Quantitative** – to show what has been achieved and how much more has to be done.

● **Worthwhile** – adding more value to the practice than they cost to collect and use.

Davies and Lampel wrote in *Quality in Health Care*:

> The challenge for the NHS is to improve quality and increase access at the same time as controlling costs and delivering value for money. The development of a plethora of performance measures in the NHS as a whole is testament to the fact that trying to pin down these three competing exigencies is an insurmountable problem. NHS primary dental care has hitherto avoided this proliferation of measures until now. There is no doubt that when gathered appropriately and accurately, acted on sensitively rather than punitively and understood by those managers who monitor services with them these performance measures can be useful. There is however a concern that performance measurement, which is in essence motivational or even coercive in nature, may in fact pervert behaviour and engender an adversarial and defensive culture detrimental to quality.

Davies *et al.* (1998).

Quantitative and qualitative measures

When looking at measures and metrics it is important that they are appropriate for the practice. It is pointless investing in the effort of collecting data simply for the sake of it and it is equally important to be able to collect the data so that it can easily be analysed without further considerable effort and time.

● Are you measuring the right thing?
● Do you have the right measures?
● Are the measures used in the right way?
● Do you determine the quality of a particular performance metric using the SMART test (Specific, Measurable, Attainable, Relevant and Timely)?

A **quantitative measure** provides a quantitative indication of the extent, amount, dimensions capacity or size of some attribute of a product or a process. As shown in Table 8, there are different types of measures.

▶ p 129.

A **qualitative measure** involves some form of direct observation of performance or indirect assessment of performance. Some examples used in dental practice include:

● observation of service delivery by peers – this is the basis of vocational training assessment such as DOPs (direct observation of procedural skill) or CEX (clinical examination exercise)
● audit of patient records
● peer review
● patient satisfaction surveys.

Measure	Description
Binomial (binary)	Like a switch, it either is or isn't (e.g. 'Is there a washer disinfector?')
Additive	Simple counts, or rates (e.g. numbers of patients seen, number of UDAs completed)
Ratio	The proportion of one value relative to another value (e.g. gross earnings per hour, number of root canal treatments provided per 100 FP17's submitted)
Averages	The mean of a population or sample data (e.g. average UDA value in a PCT area)
Statistical	Descriptive and inferential statistics (e.g. exception reports)

Monitoring your activity

Your GDS Contract or PDS Agreement will be monitored primarily in terms of UDAs. While this is the measure that is contractually agreed upon, other data will also be used by the PCT to measure activity, in addition to activity related to any additional services, such as orthodontics, domiciliaries or sedation which you may have agreed to provide. We will come to these other measures later as they are assuming an increasing importance as the contract matures.

So forget about items of service, patients on capitation, numbers registered, length of waiting list or time/sessions spent on NHS work. All those are matters for your internal practice management; the PCT should only be interested in the number of UDAs you have provided, though it is possible that your contract with them allows them to monitor other performance indicators. It is therefore important that you understand what UDAs are and what you will be expected to achieve.

If you are contracted to provide orthodontic services, then this work will be measured through UOAs. If you are contracted to provide domiciliary or sedation services these will be measured in terms of numbers of cases you see. Other services that may form part of your contract, such as dental public health services or out-of-hours dental services, will be measured in terms specified in your contract.

Monitoring by the Business Services Agency

BSA Dental Services is the paying agency for the PCT but it also undertakes to supply the PCT with a regular flow of increasingly sophisticated data, information analysis and reports on its Contractors. This information in most cases is supplied direct to the PCT, with only summary information coming to the Contractor (in the form of mid-year reviews and end of year reports). Since the PCT is only in contract with the Contractor, only patient-specific information about individual claims are sent as schedules to the Performer.

The data provided by some dental software suppliers may match some of the functions of Dental Services. Inevitably, however, the lack of some reports – particularly exception reports – makes managing the practice problematic and means the Provider has to rely on management data from the PCT on request.

Monthly schedules

The BSA will provide the necessary information to the PCT and the dentist to monitor their activity with regards the number of UDAs/UOAs performed. A monthly pay schedule will be sent containing the following information:

- the Contractor's Actual Annual Contact Value (AACV)
- the amount of the contactor's Monthly Contract Payment (MCP)
- the amount of NHS charges that the PCT has calculated should have been collected and any other deductions that need to be made to the MCP (for example, if there has been an overpayment of a previous MCP), together with the reason for any such deduction
- the amount of the MCP following these deductions
- any other payment including where relevant an indication that a particular payment is made in respect of a named dentist's Performer
- the net superannuable pay in respect of each Performer as notified to the BSA by the Contractor
- the number of UDAs or UOAs the Contractor is contracted to provide during the relevant financial year and has so far provided on the data submitted, and has left to provide during the financial year
- the number of UDAs processed by BSA Dental Services
- the number of sedations and domiciliary visits provided
- the number of exemption status patients being treated by each Performer.

The UDA as a performance measure

Rattan (2007), p 72.

Performance indicators are intended to be part of an overarching quality framework that seek to improve patient care and clinical outcomes. The UDA has been utilised by the NHS as the metric to measure performance but its inherent narrowness and its inability to assess qualitative attributes of patients care severely limits its function. Indicators should assess quality on the basis of access and effectiveness. In other words, do patients get the care they need, and is the care and treatment effective when they get it?

The UDA does none of this and its long-term future must be influenced by this limitation.

Rattan (2008).

The traditional approach to performance management in many large publicly-funded organisations has relied heavily on financial indicators and parameters. The coupling of financial resources and targets has been at the heart of performance monitoring in the new contract since its inception though its predecessor, Personal Dental Services (PDS), used other metrics to measure performance.

PCTs have relied on UDA delivery and a range of derived ratios (to include patient charge revenue, for example) as the main performance measure amongst their Contractors. This has inevitably resulted in practices not being able to reach their targets, with the result that PCTs have clawed back funds.

Without some form of quantitative measure, PCT Finance Directors are unable to ensure that they are getting the best return on their investment for maximum health gain and obtaining best value for money – a very real commissioning priority.

World Class Commissioning – Vision. December 2007 (GR 8754). Department of Health.

The real challenge in establishing 'value for money' using UDAs can be seen when comparing practices in the same PCT – if one practice is contracted to deliver 12,600 UDAs at a price of £23.60 per UDA and another is contracted to deliver 17,000 UDAs at a price of £28 per UDA, which one offers the tax payer better value for money?

It is not possible simply to rely on rudimentary metrics to answer such a complex scenario as healthcare delivery and a more balanced multi-metric approach is required to deliver long-term benefits for all the stakeholders.

Basket of measures

There is some support from the Chief Dental Officer who has supported the notion of a 'basket of indicators' and has advised PCTs that UDAs

> **are a useful way of monitoring and comparing service levels, provided they are part of a basket of indicators that capture oral health, access, quality and patient experience.**

In the Government's response to the Health Select Committee they took this further highlighting Dental Contracting and Development framework being developed by the Tees group of PCTs.

Government response to the Health Select Service Committee report on Dental Services 2008. Cm 7470 ¶24. (The Stationery Office.)

The framework includes a number of quality indicators, linked to oral health needs assessment and including preventive measures such as application of fluoride varnish and fissure sealants. The framework links to the wider public health agenda, with practices encouraged to participate in activities such as blood pressure checks. It also includes measures of patient access to dental services, availability of routine and urgent care, measures of staff training and development, and clinical governance issues.

Bradford Model Paper (tender specification), 2008.

The future of the UDA must lie in its alliance to quality. Some PCTs are moving it in this direction. For example, Bradford and Airedale PCT proposed the concept of the QDA (quality unit of dental activity) in a tender document and commissioned new services based on the following formula:

Area	Payment Mechanism	Percentage of contract income attached to area
Access	Units of Dental Activity (UDA)	60
Oral Health Improvement / Clinical Quality	Quality Unit of Dental Activity (QDA)	20
Systems, Process and Infrastructure	Dental Quality Framework (QDA)	20

Table 9: Formula for using QDAs (Bradford Model Paper).

The PCT went on to confirm that:

> It is envisaged that the balance between these three areas will change over the life of the contract with an increasing emphasis being placed on the qualitative aspects of this framework. In line with this it is anticipated that the range of quality indicators will be expanded as part of a system of continual improvement.

It is inevitable that more targets will emerge from these processes. How PCTs manage these will impact on both the service provision in a particular area and the relationship with practices who will have to work with the added bureaucracy. Table 10 shows the range of criteria proposed by the Department of Health in its guidance on contract reviews.

● p 133.
Briefing paper: NHS Dental Contract Reviews. Sep 2008. Primary Care Contracting: Web/BM/150908.

Monitoring toolkit

Primary Care Contracting has published a monitoring toolkit to support PCTs in their role to monitor NHS dental contracts. This practice visit self-assessment tool has been produced as the next stage in the development of the toolkit to assist PCTs to performance manage their NHS dental contracts. The self-assessment tool recognises that while UDAs are the main contract currency for GDS Contracts and PDS Agreements, they are only one of a range of indicators that PCTs may wish to use to monitor and manage dental services.

In their description of this toolkit, the PCC advise PCTs that:

> Units of dental activity (which are a weighted measure of courses of treatment) are a useful way of monitoring and comparing service levels, provided they are part of a basket of indicators that measure oral health, access, quality and patient experience.

Practice Self assessment tools for NHS General and Personal Dental Services Contractors. Primary Care Contracting. www.pcc.nhs.uk/163.php#Performance_Management

Quantitative criteria	Qualitative criteria
● Activity ● Value for money ● Waiting times for new patients ● Spread of patient base ● Any change of patient mix ● DRO & DPA reports/outcomes ● Percentage of patients re-attending within 3 months and 3-9 months to check contractual compliance with NICE guidelines ● Exception reports: issues being reported and the practice's response to the reports ● Referrals to secondary care: type and volume ● Compliance with Standards for Better Health ● Opening hours ● Number of new patients seen in previous 2 years ● Percentage of patients with band 1 urgent course of treatment	● Complaints & compliments: numbers/trends and the response of the Contractor ● User experience: does the practice ask patients about their perceptions and experience of the service they receive? ● Patient satisfaction: percentage of patients satisfied with treatment received and percentage satisfied with waiting time for appointment ● Whether the PCT has had any cause for concern about the practice and how the practice responded ● Practice infrastructure ● Capital funding: whether any capital money allocated by the PCT was used well/appropriately to develop the practice ● Clinical governance activity undertaken ● Oral health and access: to what extent is the practice delivering the service that its customers need/want? ● GDC investigation

Table 10: Quantitative and qualitative criteria for contract reviews (Department of Health).

12 CONTRACT REVIEWS

This chapter looks at the performance reviews that a PCT should carry out at mid-year and annually. It also looks at end-of-year issues and how PCTs interpret the data they receive about you.

The PCT monitors your performance on a monthly basis and may well contact you if your UDA totals are well off target. However, the contract allows for two formal reviews of activity: one after 30 September and the other after the subsequent 31 March.

Mid-year reviews

By 31 October the PCT is informed of the number of UDAs completed by all its dentists. The target that needs to be achieved at this mid-year point is at least 30 per cent of the total number of UDAs that the practice as a whole has to provide. If you have fallen short of the 30 per cent target, the PCT will notify you in writing, setting out the number of UDAs that you have achieved – according to its records – and the percentage of the total this represents. They may well invite you to participate in a formal review of your activity which could be a face to face meeting with the PCT.

At this meeting you are entitled to bring any written material which the PCT must consider. You may be able to demonstrate that you have performed more UDAs than the PCT has recorded. Notes of the meeting are kept and confirmed by both parties. In these circumstances, the usefulness of having your own information about the number of UDAs completed by the practice should be self-evident. If the only information you have to rely on is from either the PCT or the BSA, it will be difficult to persuade the PCT that you have performed more UDAs than it has recorded.

An example of the particular problems that can occur relate to the transmission of claims via EDI where electronic forms are sent but not received by BSA Dental Services. You are advised to print out transmission reports when claims are sent by WebEDI.

Practice-based computer software, for instance from Software of Excellence and Kodak R4, produce a range of reports in real time. These provide evidence on, for example, the number of UDAs completed by the practice and by each individual Performer and the total number of UDAs treatment planned but not yet completed (i.e. work in progress). This information will enable you to outline with some accuracy how likely you are to achieve the PCT's targets in the short term. Working in the 2006 contract will become increasingly difficult without ICT. There is no compulsion on the PCT to accept your explanation for any shortfalls in activity at the mid-year review.

What the PCT can do at mid-year

If the PCT has serious concerns about your ability to achieve the number of UDAs you are contracted to do, it can do one of three things.

1) It can require you to comply with a written plan (drawn up by the PCT) to ensure that the level of activity during the remainder of the financial year will allow the Contractor to achieve the requisite number of UDAs.
2) It can withhold money.
3) It can agree with you to reduce the total number of UDAs required to be achieved under the contract, with the appropriate adjustment in contract value.

Ⓡ NHS (GDS Contracts) 2005 P6 S3 P8 ¶59(1–5).

If the PCT withholds money there is a formula that dictates what the maximum amount is:

> **If x is the amount payable for the year for all the completed UDAs and y is the amount payable for the six months' worth of UDAs actually achieved by the Contractor between 1 April and 30 September and z is the amount of money withheld then the maximum the PCT can withhold at this mid-year review is:**
>
> $$z = x - (y \times 2)$$

Any money that is withheld by the PCT will be paid back in full at the end of the year if you achieve the required number of UDAs contracted for.

If the Contractor gives three months' notice of termination of the contract at the mid-year review point, the PCT can still withhold money until there has been a reconciliation of the total number of UDAs/UOAs achieved by the Contractor against the contract value received. It is nearly always the

Mid Year Reviews. BDA Advice Note 83, August 2006.

case that the Contractor will have to repay money to the PCT for UDAs not achieved.

Annual report and review

Once a year, by 30 June, the PCT are required to prepare an annual report on your contract. It will be based on information from forms you have submitted, rather like the existing practice profile. The report will include:

- the Actual Annual Contract Value for the previous year
- the total amount of deductions including the NHS charges
- the net superannuable pay of each Performer in the practice
- the number of UDAs/UOAs you agreed to provide
- the number actually provided
- any outstanding UDAs (or UOAs) not provided.

Since the contractual requirements are quite wide-ranging, the scope of any annual review that PCTs will make could be extensive and time-consuming. However, the PCT will need to ensure that any information they need to provide for a monitoring visit is sent in advance to the Contractor for review. In the first year of the contract the recommendation to PCTs was to 'apply a light touch' when it came to performance monitoring, in recognition of the fact that the new arrangements represented a significant departure from the old system. PCTs were encouraged to

approach contract reviews in a supportive and facilitative way and to seek to understand how Contractors are delivering the activity.

Dental Contract Review Process: 'Hints and Tips' (2006). Primary Care Contracting.

PCTs will consider the following issues:

- the timeliness of the submission of FP17 forms, which may result in an understatement of UDA/UOA activity and income from patient charges
- the resources and investment required for PCTs to build and develop effective relationships with NHS dentists
- ensuring a consistent and fair approach to monitoring all dental contracts, including PCT salaried services, independent Contractors, out-of-hours Contractors and dental access centres
- ensuring the minimum of burden on Contractors and their staff to prepare for the monitoring meetings and review
- other information, such as:
  - quantitative and qualitative information, including monthly Dental Services activity and finance reports (e.g. looking at the number of courses of treatment in each band compared with other years and benchmarks)
  - patient feedback

Note: Unless there is a contractual agreement to achieve a certain level of PCR, the PCT cannot penalise a practice which fails to reach this target if they have achieved the contracted number of UDAs (the amount collected in patient charges was considerably less than that expected).

- information from Patient Advice and Liaison Service/ complaints
- compliance with clinical governance protocols
- recommendations from dental practice advisers
- visits from the Dental Reference Service

- monitoring the patient charge revenue (PCR) collected by the practice via patient charges and comparing it to the test period for each practice

- examining the practice's total UDA number divided by the PCR by the practice at any one time: this will give the amount of patient charge revenue that is collected for every UDA (some practices may be more 'valuable' than others to the PCT as money generators in the future)

- looking at other ratios such as the mix of charge paying and exempt patients and comparing them with previous contract years to assess whether there is a change in patient profile which may reflect demographic changes in the area or be an intended practice objective.

Once you have had time to consider this and discuss it within the practice, an annual review will take place. In most circumstances this will be a simple process, possibly a single phone call, and should not take up too much of your time. The PCT will prepare a draft record of the review for your comments before producing a final written record of the review. This will be sent to you.

The review is an opportunity for you and the PCT to discuss any problems that have arisen, agree any adjustments to your contract and talk over any plans that you or the PCT may have for the future. For instance, you might want to reduce or expand your NHS commitment. The PCT might ask if you could provide any additional services to help it deliver its commitment to improving the oral health of its population.

The PCT may also look at how any complaints have been handled, compliance with Health and Safety Regulations and NICE guidance. It will want to ensure that all Performers are registered and on a PCT Performers List. The Performers must also be up to date with their continuing professional development requirements and have indemnity protection. In a document issued in relation to capital funding in July 2006, the Department of Health gave PCTs a bullet point list that effectively established the criteria by which a practice's NHS commitment can be judged:

- evidence of flexible patient access to the practice (e.g. willingness to provide access to new patients, willingness to take referrals from patients who have contacted PCT access helplines, flexibility in providing appointment slots across the normal range of practice opening hours)

- providing services for a full range of patients (unless the practice is a specialist practice)
- the current condition and suitability of premises
- compliance with PCT clinical governance and quality assurance
- evidence that services are provided in accordance with NICE guidelines on patient recall intervals.

You may want to carry out your own audit. This could also be a good time to produce a business plan for the medium-term development of your practice, not just the next year. You might want to take on new more patients, provide additional services, such as advanced mandatory services. You might also want the PCT to invest capital in the practice.

Year-end statement of activity

A sample copy of a year-end activity report is available at: www.nhsbsa.nhs.uk/DentalServices/ Documents/year_end_contract_report_ example.pdf.

The BSA is required by the Statement of Financial Entitlement to produce an 'annual reconciliation report'. This provides both the Contractor and the PCT with details of:

- the Annual Contract Value
- the total value of deductions made over the year, with patient charges revenue reported separately
- the estimated net pensionable earnings of each Performer
- the number of UDAs/UOAs contacted
- the number of UDAs/UOAs scheduled
- the variation between the contracted and the scheduled UDAs/ UOAs
- the number of courses of treatment involving sedation or domiciliary services.

This year-end statement of activity from Dental Services will come in the July schedules to the practice. A copy of this is sent electronically to your PCT to inform and support the year-end review process. However, this information is not sent directly to the Performers: it is for the Contractors to pass on the relevant information and trends to the Performers where necessary.

It is worth taking time to consider the information within the statement of activity. It contains an excellent overview of how your practice is performing in the contract, allowing you to compare it against your PCT, your Strategic Health Authority and national benchmarks.

There are five tables in total. The first three tables provide breakdowns of scheduled UDA activity by patient status, charge band and patient charge status by charge band. A further table shows the percentage of UDA activity for:

Guidance for Year-End Statement of Activity. GR: NHS BSA/DSD/0007. BSA Dental Services Division.

- incomplete treatment
- free repair/replacements

- late submitted FP17s
- continuation treatments
- treatment on referrals
- Regulation 11 (replacement of appliances such orthodontic braces which have been replaced and the patient charged accordingly).

Some of these are important when we look at exception reporting (see page 143), so it is useful to compare your own practice's activity profile against the average in the PCT, SHA and country. (Practices in England are benchmarked against practices in England separately from those in Wales which have their own benchmarks.)

The clinical data set information which also compares your practice with the rest of England is also very useful as it gives the number of each item claimed and the rate of claim per 100 FP17s. This is based on the data entered in Part 5a of the FP17, a mandatory field that has to be completed every time a claim is made. Most computer systems will complete this automatically if clinical treatment records are kept electronically.

Part 5a Clinical Data Set

Scale & polish	1		Fluoride varnish	2		Fissure sealants	3	No. of teeth	Radiograph(s) taken	4	Enter No.
Endodontic treatment	5	No. of teeth	Permanent fillings & Sealant restorations	6	No. of teeth	Extractions	7	No. of teeth	Crown(s) provided	8	No. of teeth
Upper denture - Acrylic	9	No. of teeth	Lower denture - Acrylic	A	No. of teeth	Upper denture - Metal	B	No. of teeth	Lower denture - Metal	C	No. of teeth
Veneer(s) applied	D	No. of teeth	Inlay(s)	E	No. of teeth	Bridge(s) fitted	F	No. of units	Referral for advanced mandatory services	G	

Figure 17: Part 5a of the FP17.

End of year issues

In order to ensure that the practice does not over-deliver or under-deliver on its contracted UDAs, careful monitoring of activity, particularly in the last few weeks of each financial year, is crucial. This is especially relevant to a practice with several Performers, some of whom may work part time. It is important to realise also that you have two months from the date of completion within which to send off the FP17 forms for scheduling.

While the contract allows for under-performance of up to 4 per cent – which must be made up in no less than 60 days (the PCT may allow more at its discretion) – there are no regulations on over-performance. Many PCTs simply refuse to pay Contractors whose practices have over-performed on their contract.

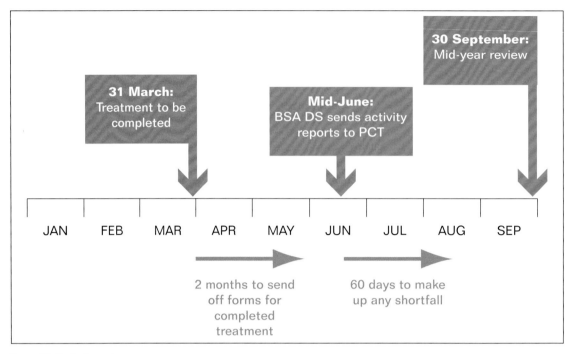

Figure 18: End of year issues

It is important to recognise what the qualification criteria are for UDAs/ UOAs to be included in the current financial year rather than the next. This will influence whether a patient's treatment should be completed or not started at all before 1 April; this decision is also likely to be influenced by whether the practice is ahead or behind on its target.

Dental Services will apply the following criteria to assess whether the activity data submitted on a FP17 will qualify for inclusion in the current financial year's report or the next.

Technical guidance relating to end of year activity and patient charge revenue.
www.nhsbsa.nhs.uk/DentalServices/ Documents/guidance_amends.pdf.

- all activity data collected from FP17s scheduled in any of the 12 schedule months from the April of the preceding year
- all activity data collected from FP17s scheduled in the April and May of the current year that have a treatment completion date prior to 1 April
- all activity data collected from FP17s, which were received by 31 May of the current year with a treatment completion date prior to 1 April and scheduled
- amendments to previously scheduled FP17s that were received and processed up to the scheduling date of the contract in June of the current year.

Where FP17s do not have a date of completion, for instance because the patient failed to return to complete the treatment, the following assumption will be applied: if the acceptance date for the course of treatment is on or before 31 March and it was received and scheduled by the DPD within the 31 May deadline, the DPD will place that activity in the current reporting year.

In simplified form this means:

Table 11: Timing of activities.

Timing of activity	Will it count for this year's activity?
Treatment started and finished by 31 March	Yes
Treatment started by 31 March but completed in April and by 31 May	No
Treatment started on or before 31 March but designated incomplete and received and scheduled by BSA by 31 May	Yes

If requested, Dental Services will send Contractors CDs containing all activity on the end of year statement. It is the Contractor's responsibility to highlight errors: to faciliate this, it is recommended that activity should be reconciled throughout the year using the monthly schedules.

Under-delivery of UDAs

As already stated, the contract regulations allow Contractors to under-deliver by up to 4 per cent of the annual UDA/UOA target, as long as that shortfall is made good the following year. (In the first year of the contract many of the underperforming practices were small contracts or child-only contracts.) Your PCT cannot take any action if you agree to make up the units within a time period of not less than 60 days.

If you are well behind on your quota of UDAs during the year, your PCT will want to discuss this with you. There may be valid reasons why this happens: for instance, if you have had a period of sickness or maternity leave or a Performer has left and it has taken a long time to find a replacement. The PCT could decide not to vary the contract if it feels that this was a one-off. Alternatively, the PCT can vary the number of UDAs you are required to deliver under your contract, with a concomitant change in the contract value.

In order to make this change the PCT will need to give you notice in writing of this contract variation. First, however, you and the PCT must discuss the issue and try to come to an agreed way forward. In the words of the Regulations, 'both parties shall use their best endeavours to communicate and co-operate with each other with a view to determining what (if any) variation' in UDAs is needed.

Risk management information

The PCT is able to obtain risk management information from Dental Services to assess Performers and Contractors and identify those regarded as higher risk who would then merit enhanced monitoring. Automated and manual checks will include:

- examining practice record cards
- comparing treatment patterns of Performers
- checking treatment history and identity of patients
- identifying the accuracy of patient charges levied by Performers using a range of tools including patients' questionnaires
- projected numbers of UDAs or UOAs that will be achieved if the current rate continues for the remainder of the financial year – should that projection fall outside the 4 per cent tolerance range, a warning message will appear in the information report sent to the PCT.

Inappropriate activity – 'gaming'

Managing suspicions of fraud in General/Personal Dental Services. February 2007. (Counter Fraud and Security Management Services)

BSA Dental Services recognises that the opportunities for inappropriate financial gain for Contractors and Performers are limited. Contract values are agreed in advance and only subject to variation with the express agreement of the PCT. There are however opportunities to maximise the units of dental and orthodontic activity – euphemistically termed 'finessing' the system or 'gaming' – to reduce a Contractor's obligation under the contract.

The well recognised ways of doing this are as follows

- splitting courses of treatment (especially for exempt patients)
- providing urgent treatment followed by a banded course of treatment
- reporting incomplete or abandoned courses of treatment
- treating or assessing the same patients too frequently
- inappropriate referrals within the same practice
- inappropriate claiming of charge-exempt items (e.g. prescriptions, guaranteed treatments, continuation treatments).

McCallum (2007).

It is not Dental Service's role to determine the causes for apparently unusual behaviour, but rather to report the matter to the PCT. The PCT – using their local knowledge, detailed understanding of the contract agreement and possibly awareness of other concerns that have been raised – can then assess the level of risk and decide whether and what further actions are necessary and appropriate.

The only exception to this would be where there appears to be evidence of fraud. In these cases a referral to the Counter Fraud and Security Management Services will be made. Fraudulent activity includes:

- recording the wrong band and associated charge
- submitting FP17s for non-existent 'ghost' patients

- deliberately falsifying records
- reporting non-existent courses of treatment
- claiming false entitlement to free treatment (this could be a false claim by either the patient or the dentist).

The risk areas for PCTs include:

- Contractors delaying submission of FP17s – this provides a temporary increase in cash flow as patient charges have been collected but not deducted
- inadequate or incorrect declaration of patient exemption status – this reduces patients' charge revenue.

Ultimately in any system of remuneration there needs to be a high degree of trust in the professionals that work in it. This is largely well placed, since dentists and their teams strive to provide high quality care for their patients. Any contractual currency, whether it is based on fee-per-item, capitation or (as under the current system) courses of treatment, has ultimately to rely on dentists delivering care to meet clinical need, and not allowing their judgement to be affected by the degree of remuneration that an individual treatment will attract.

Government response to the Health Select Committee Report on Dental Services. Cm 7470 October 2008 p 10 ¶39.

Exception reporting

Exception reporting is the selection and highlighting of FP17 claims that are in some way different or critical. Results that fall outside a set of predetermined threshold values – exceptions – are automatically highlighted: this enables a PCT to identify immediately any results that deviate from the expected results. This is an essential part of performance monitoring and PCTs receive quarterly exception reports on all Contractors in their area.

One particular area of concern is higher than expected incidence of charge-free items appearing in practice profiles:

- continuation of treatment
- charge-free repair or replacements of certain restorations, e.g. filling, root filling, porcelain veneer or crown
- prescription-only treatments.

In all these cases, the patient is not charged but UDAs are earned by the Contractor. There are clear rules governing when and in what circumstances these claims can be made legitimately but PCTs need to identify instances whether they are being claimed incorrectly out of ignorance or guile and have been given advice on how to do this.

Briefing note – Monitoring local dental contracts: how to manage a high incidence of charge free items on monitoring reports. October 2006. (Primary Care Contracting)

The other categories reported under exception reporting are:

- no activity
- low activity
- late reporting

- multiple FP17s
- urgent Band 1 treatments
- adult patient mix comparing fee-paying with exempt which shows a change in profile of the patients being treated by a practice.

Vital signs

The NHS in England: The Operating Framework for 2008/9. 13 December 2007 (GR 9120). Department of Health.

In December 2007 the Department of Health published the NHS Operating Framework 2008/9. It set a clear strategic objective for PCTs to improve, year-on-year, the number of patients accessing NHS dental services. This then became the new metric for PCT to chase, in addition to ensuring the practices met their annual UDA targets. The key performance indicator (KPI) was the number of people receiving primary dental services within the most recent 24-month period in comparison with March 2006.

The specific metrics to be used were:

- the change in 24-month access for each practice since the last quarter
- the UDAs delivered versus the number commissioned
- the UDAs delivered in relation to the profile across the bands
- the UDAs compared with the England average.

From July 2008 these vital signs reports began arriving electronically in PCT offices throughout England, providing further information and incentives to PCTs to improve access.

These reports come as tables with RAG (Red, Amber, Green) status indicators with parameters. For example, with 24-month access targets the contract was badged as 'Red' if there had been a decrease of 1 per cent or more, 'Amber' if the change was between -1 per cent to 2 per cent and 'Green' if the change was an increase of 2 per cent or more since the last quarter.

Quarterly Vital Signs Reports BSA GR NHSBSA/DSD/0008.

There are three areas that the Vital signs reports on: **access**, **activity** and **quality**.

Access

The measure provides a count for each Contractor of the number of distinct patient identities where their most recent course of treatment (scheduled during the last 24 months) was with that Contractor. This metric is an indication of the number of unique patients that are considered NHS patients of the practice (though of course they are not technically considered to be 'registered' with the practice). The access figures are provided at quarterly points from March 2008, though the PCT level report will show the number of patients who were registered with the practice at the end of the old contract in March 2006. This is effectively the baseline for a Contractor's list size.

Activity

At a practice level this will show the total number of UDAs/UOAs commissioned from the Contractor and then their position at each quarter in relation to that target.

Quality

The concept of quality being measured by Dental Services in this section does not relate to clinical quality or necessarily quality of the service provided, but instead what is perceived to be the quality of the administrative management of the contract. The following measures are currently being used though over time these will be changed and added to.

- **Percentage of FP17s for the same patient ID re-attending within 3 months**
  This measure is reported as, in general, a patient who has completed a course of treatment that renders him or her 'dentally fit' should not need to see a dentist again within the next three months. The measure reports the percentage of FP17s for the same patient identity where the previous course of treatment for that patient ID ended three months or less prior to the most recent course of treatment for that patient ID.

- **Percentage of FP17s for the same patient ID re-attending between 3 months and 9 months**
  This measure reports the percentage of FP17s for the same patient identity where the previous course of treatment for that patient ID was ended between 31 and 90 days prior to the most recent course of treatment for that patient ID.

The main reason for choosing these first two metrics is to establish whether Contractors are 'churning' the same healthy patients. In the case of patients attending within three months it is less likely that they will attend within a short period of time after completing a course of treatment that has secured their oral health. Where they do attend in pain, with a broken filling or trauma, the clinical records need to reflect this. In this way, any investigation of the records will confirm that the patient has attended for justifiable reasons and not simply because the course of treatment has been artificially split.

Dentists face curb on abuse of salary system. The Independent 13 October 2008.

In the case of patients attending between three and nine months this measure is designed to measure how many patients are being recalled at six months and therefore by implication a Contractor's failure to comply with NICE guidelines (this would represent a breach of the contract). The reality is that the figures measure all types of activity, not just recalls, and include urgent treatment, orthodontic treatment or assessments and

Band 2 and 3 treatments. This is therefore a rather blunt instrument with which to check recalls intervals. Furthermore, the NICE guidelines, while confirming that each patient should have a recall set individually depending on their specific needs, offers no percentage figures as to how many patients should be recalled at the various intervals ranging from 3 to 24 months in any particular practice setting. In addition, there is still not enough evidence to support or refute the long-established practice of encouraging patients to attend for dental check-ups at six-monthly intervals.

Beirne *et al.* (2007).

- ● **Percentage of FP17s for Band 1 urgent courses of treatment**
  This is a measure of the percentage of FP17s scheduled where the patient charge band was Band 1 urgent. A high proportion of Band 1 urgents may indicate an issue with the quality of diagnosis or treatment planning; conversely, a very low proportion of Band 1 urgent may indicate that patients are not able to access urgent treatment.

The decision as to when it is appropriate to claim an urgent treatment is still subject to wide interpretation, even within the limits of the definition of urgent treatment. For example, it is common for a patient to attend in pain and be treated under urgent treatment when root canal treatment is initiated with pulp extirpation. This on its own will allow the course of treatment to be deemed as urgent. However, if the patient returns to see the practice for continuation and completion of the root canal treatment, it is debatable whether a Band 2 treatment should be started at the next visit (i.e. an urgent treatment followed by a Band 2 treatment) or whether the whole course of treatment qualifies for a Band 2 charge. (This could be argued, as the patient expressed a preference to return to complete the treatment.)

Contractors may have arranged with PCTs to provide access slots and this may explain a high incidence of urgent treatment claimed. The real implication for PCTs with Contractors claiming urgent treatment is that it attracts 1.2 UDAs, while the patient is only charged the same as a Band 1 course of treatment. This leads to a reduction in patient charge revenue overall, particularly where urgent treatments are claimed with another course of treatment on the same patient and the patient is exempt from charges.

- ● **Percentage of FP17s relating to free repair or replacements**
  This is a measure of the percentage of FP17s scheduled where treatment was provided as a free repair or replacement item. A high percentage of free repairs or replacements may indicate an issue with the quality of treatment being provided; conversely, no free repairs or replacements over a period of time may indicate that patients are having difficulty accessing this service.

- **Percentage of FP17s relating to continuations**

  This is a measure of the percentage of FP17s scheduled where treatment was provided as a continuation of a previous same or higher banded course of treatment. A high percentage of continuation treatment may indicate an issue with the diagnosis, planning or quality of treatment being provided. Conversely, no continuations over a period of time may indicate that patients are having difficulty accessing this service.

The real concern for PCTs is the danger that treatment plans are being artificially spilt to maximise the utilisation of UDAs, such that a patient's treatment is terminated without completing the course of treatment. The patient is then seen again within two months to complete the outstanding treatment but on a new course of treatment: although the patient is not charged again the Contractor is still eligible to claim UDAs.

- **Percentage of patients satisfied with the dentistry they have received.**

  ♦ Annex, p 148.

  This measure is derived from the results of the DSD's routine random patient questionnaires. The results of these are reported quarterly at PCT level to PCTs. It provides the patients' view of dental quality. The analysis each quarter is based on responses to questionnaires sent to a random sample of over 25,000 patients. The national response rate (the proportion of questionnaires completed and returned by patients) is currently around 50 per cent.

- **Qualitative monitoring**

  The PCT monitoring of quality externally comes from the patient questionnaires. It will also use complaints or queries raised to PALS to monitor both the quality of the service as well as compliance with the regulations.

Many patients who use the PCT or PALS as a point of information about their care and treatment do not always wish to raise an official complaint against the practice either because they are in the middle of treatment or because they want to continue to remain 'registered' with the practice because of the difficulty in accessing NHS services elsewhere.

Common areas of concern for patients revolve around:

- treatment not available on the NHS – e.g. bridges, molar endodontics
- inferior quality of NHS treatment
- insisting on assessment before making decision whether or not to provide NHS treatment
- applying a booking fee or charging for missed appointments or short notice cancellations
- patient told that 'extensive treatment' is only available privately
- UDAs only for exempt and children.

Dental Services

PQS01 / 07/01/09 / 0307678236X

NHS Dentistry Patient Survey

Please help us to monitor NHS dental services by completing this questionnaire and returning it in the freepost envelope provided. Additional comments or information should not be written on this form - if necessary please attach a separate sheet.

Q1. Did you visit the dentist between   26/11/2008   & 15/12/2008   ?

Yes ☐   No ☐   Cannot remember ☐

Q2. Did you visit the dentist at Dental Surgery, 7 Any Street, Any Town, AA2 3BB
?

Yes ☐   No ☐   Cannot remember ☐

Q3. Was the following information about you correct at the time you last visited the dentist?

Name: Julie T-----   Yes ☐   No ☐

Date of birth: dd/mm/yyyy   Yes ☐   No ☐

Q4. Did you have? (Tick **one** box)

Just NHS treatment ☐   Combination of NHS and private treatment ☐

All private treatment ☐   Unsure ☐

Q5. Were you given a written treatment plan?   Yes ☐   No ☐   Not sure ☐

Q6. What **NHS** treatment did you have? (Tick all that apply)

Examination ☐	X-rays(s) ☐	Scale & polish ☐	Filling(s) ☐
Root filling(s) ☐	Crown(s) ☐	Extraction(s) ☐	Denture(s) ☐
Bridge(s) ☐	Sedation ☐	Orthodontic ☐	Veneers ☐
Other ☐			

CONTINUED OVER THE PAGE

INVESTOR IN PEOPLE

Supporting the NHS, supplying the NHS, protecting the NHS
NHS Dental Services is a service provided by the NHS Business Services Authority

Q7. Did you pay a charge for your NHS treatment?

☐ No

☐ Yes How much did you pay for your NHS treatment? £_____:_____p

           Which band was your treatment? ☐ 1 ☐ 2 ☐ 3 ☐ Don't know

           Were you given a receipt? ☐ Yes ☐ No ☐ Cannot remember

Q8. Did you see any information about patient charges for NHS dentistry at the surgery?

        ☐ Yes ☐ No ☐ Cannot remember

Q9. How do you feel about the length of time taken to get an appointment with the dentist?
(Tick **one** box)

    It was as soon as was necessary ☐

    It should have been a bit sooner ☐

    It should have been much sooner ☐

Q10. How satisfied are you with the NHS dentistry you received? (Tick **one** box)

    Completely satisfied ☐ Fairly satisfied ☐

    Fairly dissatisfied ☐ Very dissatisfied ☐

Please use the pre-paid envelope supplied to return your completed questionnaire. If you have lost the envelope, you can post this form to: Patient Questionnaires, NHSBSA Dental Services, Compton Place Road, Eastbourne, East Sussex BN20 8XX

5AA 123456/0001/123456

Left and above: from the NHS BSA's NHS Dentistry Patient Survey

13 DISPUTES, SANCTIONS AND APPEALS

This chapter describes the various sanctions that a PCT can apply to a Contractor and how contracts can be varied. It also looks at the effects of contract breaches and termination.

Dispute resolution

The fundamental difference between the old GDS system and the current one is the contractual relationship between the dentist and the PCT. This means that unlike the old GDS system, where contracts could be terminated only where the Contractor had breached his terms of service or had sanctions applied by courts (criminal action) or regulatory bodies (the GDC), the new regulations also allows for the PDS contracts to be terminated within a fixed time frame. This is in line with other primary care Contractors' contracts such as general medical practitioners, pharmacists and optometrists.

◆ Chapter 2, 'Setting the scene', p 9. Since the 1990 Act, Part 1 services have been provided by NHS trusts created under the National Health Service and Community Care Act 1990. These bodies became the 'Contractors' of services. While general dental practice was a Part 2 Contractor within this regulation it became a Part 1 Contractor following the Health and Social Care (Community Health and Standards) Act 2003. This meant it entered a cash-limited system.

Most important of all is the status of the NHS contract itself which does not operate within the same terms of reference as classic English contract law, containing as it does a voluntary element and lacking the constraints affecting the operation of ordinary market forces.

The Regulations allow the contactor to elect to be regarded as a health service Contractor for the purposes of Section 4 of the 1990 Act. If a Contractor does this, the contract between himself and the PCT will be regarded as an NHS contract and will therefore not be enforceable in the courts. In any case, even if both parties are not considered health service bodies they may refer any dispute to the Secretary of State to consider and determine the matter.

The 1990 Act defines the NHS contract as an

> arrangement under which one health service body (the 'acquirer') arranges for the provision to it by another health service body (the 'Provider') of goods and services which it reasonably requires for the purposes of its functions'

Critically the Act provides that:

> Whether or not an arrangement which constitutes an NHS contract would apart from this subsection, be a contract in law, it shall not be regarded for any purpose as giving rise to contractual rights or liabilities, but if any dispute arises with respect to such an arrangement, either party may refer the matter to the Secretary of State for determination under the following provisions of this section (s4(3)).

Hughes (1990).

Use of the courts to resolve contractual disputes is ruled out. Parties will be required to submit to mandatory conciliation by the strategic health authorities, followed if necessary by binding arbitration by the Health Secretary or their appointee, who has the power to impose 'directions'. These include directions regarding payments needed to give effect to variation or termination, and must be treated as if they were the result of agreement between the parties themselves. (This in fact goes well beyond the powers of judges in contract cases.)

A dentist may elect not to have the contract deemed as an NHS contract, but it is not clear in that case whether a court of law could be asked to adjudicate. In some cases considerable sums of money may be involved, increasing the potential for pre-contract disputes as well as disputes arising at mid-year reviews. Significantly, if money is to be withheld by the PCT for the non-performance of the contract, then parties other than the Contractor may be affected, including Performers and staff employed by the practice.

Actions by the PCT

It is important to recognise that any action taken by the PCT in relation to the performance of the contract will usually be directed towards the Contractor who will be the Provider. Performers will be subject to action by the PCT not through the contract but by virtue of the NHS (Performers List) Regulations 2004, as amended by the National Health Service (Performers Lists) Amendment Regulations 2005.

This creates particular problems for practice owners in that any breaches of the contract may be a result of something a Performer has or has not done, but they as Contractors will be held responsible. Contractors and Performers should ensure that they have contracts that cover issues of performance and compliance with NHS regulations and contractual obligations which are wider ranging.

A number of issues have arisen since the start of the 2006 contract. These are being dealt with by PCTs using the various process discussed later in this section. They include:

- under-activity of UDAs below the 4 per cent tolerance level
- selectively withdrawing from providing certain treatments on the NHS such as chrome dentures, molar endodontics and bridges
- misleading patients about the availability of services on the NHS
- only accepting certain categories of new patients, e.g. children, exempt adults
- changing the profile of the practice over time
- failing to comply with health and safety standards
- failing to comply with clinical governance issues (e.g. poor record keeping).

Variation without consent

(R) NHS (General Dental Services Contracts) 2005 P6 S3 P9 ¶60 (2)

There is a proviso within the regulations that specifically allows the PCT to vary the contract within 14 days of written notice. This is only when it needs to comply with the NHS Act, any regulations made pursuant to it (e.g. GDS Regulations, Dental Charges regulations, NHS Performers List Regulations) or any direction given by the Secretary of State for Health pursuant to the NHS Act.

Commentators have pointed out that this particular clause shows how vulnerable Contractors are to the whims of government and how easily the contract can be varied within a very short space of time. It is suggested that goodwill values could be wiped out instantly and that it would be unwise to base business plans on such rocky foundations.

Variation of contract in relation to UDA activity

Standard contract, clauses 289–92.

Both the Contractor and the PCT can vary the number of UDAs or UOAs to be provided under the contract. This allows the Contractor or the PCT to reduce the number of UDAs. It usually comes into play when the Contractor is struggling to meet the targets: rather than continue to an inevitable shortfall at the end of the financial year, it may be appropriate to make an in-year adjustment. This variation may be temporary or, more likely, permanent.

The adjustment will lead to a reduction in contract value: it is for the PCT to decide whether it uses the practice's UDA value or its own valuation – perhaps the PCT average – to determine this.

Practices going private have used this mechanism to reduce their NHS capacity gradually in a series of contract variations with the PCT over time.

Whether it is the Contractor or the PCT which decides to implement this contract variation, the other party must be informed in writing. In any case the commissioner cannot vary the contract without permission from the Provider.

Managing contract failure

Breach notices

Breach notices can be issued when a Contractor has breached the civil contract and the breach is not capable of remedy. Examples of this include:

- going on holiday and failing to make adequate provision to see patients urgently who are under a current course of treatment
- refusing to provide services that should be made available under a mandatory services contract (e.g. molar endodontics, chrome dentures)
- failing to issue an FP17DC for the appropriate courses of treatment
- failing to achieve contractually agreed UDA targets.

A PCT's purpose in issuing a breach notice is to warn the Contractor and to advise that any repetition of the breach may result in further action, such as termination.

A breach notice should be taken seriously if you want to remain with the NHS. Some breaches may have an ethical or professional dimension which may result in a referral of the matter to the GDC, the Counter Fraud Service or the Security Management Service (both operated by the NHS Business Services Authority). The process for managing breaches is shown in Figure 19.

▶ p 154.

Remedial notices

In contrast to breaches notices, remedial notices advise the Contractor to rectify a contract failure that *can* be remedied. Examples of these may include replacing infection control equipment that may not be adequate (e.g. autoclaves).

The Regulations set out specific features that any remedial notice issued by the PCT must contain:

- details of the breach
- the steps the Contractor must take to the satisfaction of the PCT in order to remedy the breach
- the 'notice period' – i.e. the period during which the steps must be taken.

This notice period should be no less than 28 days from the date the notice is given, unless a shorter period is necessary either to protect the safety of the Contractor's patients or protect the PCT from material financial loss.

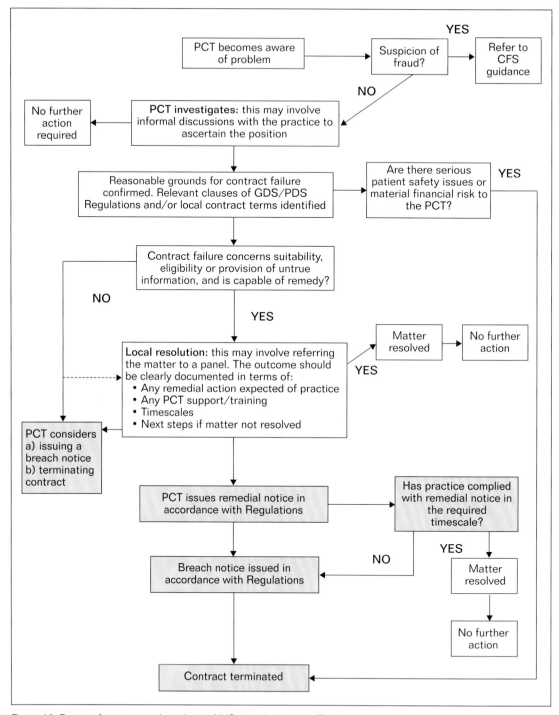

Figure 19: Process for managing breaches in NHS dental contracts. The boxes in blue are mandatory parts of the GDS/PDS regulations. (Diagram from *Handling Breaches of NHS Dentistry Contract*, June 2007, p 5. (Primary Care Contracting).)

Handling breaches

Handling breaches on NHS Dentistry Contracts, June 2007. (Primary Care Contracting)

In advice set out by the Department of Health to PCTs there are two main types of performance issue that may give rise to a breach:

1) behaviour that gives cause for concern, which may (or may not) lead to
2) failure to deliver the contract.

The Department's advice goes on to set out possible scenarios that the PCT may encounter:

- contract failure (either a breach of the GDS/PDS contract regulations and/or locally agreed contract terms) that is capable of being rectified
- contract failure, but PCT has major concerns
- contract failure, but PCT has minor concerns
- contract failure – serious risks to patient safety that it is reasonable for the contract to be terminated immediately
- the Contractor's financial situation is such that the PCT considers that it is at risk of material financial loss, and therefore that it is reasonable for the contract to terminated immediately.

A 'stepwise' approach to managing contract breaches is envisaged (Figure 20). In this way, where a local discussion between the PCT and the Contractors resolves the problem, more formal measures can be avoided.

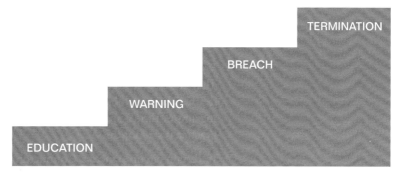

Figure 20: Visualising the 'stepwise' approach to managing contract breaches.

If the Contractor is either unable to remedy the breach by the end of the notice period or repeats the breach, the PCT may serve notice to terminate the contract.

Termination by the PCT

The issue of a termination notice is quite clearly a serious step. It is likely to affect the livelihoods of not just the Contractor but Performers and support staff such as dental nurses and practice managers. There will be effects on dental technicians and others, including family members. It is a power that PCTs need to utilise appropriately, proportionally and reasonably within the confines of public law.

The Department of Health's advice note to PCTs identifies a number of situations in which a contract may be terminated by giving written notice to the Contractor. The PCT can terminate the Contractor's contract automatically in the following circumstances:

- The Contractor agrees.
- The Contractor dies.
- The Contractor ceases to be a dental practitioner by virtue of suspension from the GDC register or erasure.
- The Contractor is unsuitable for a variety of reasons such as being convicted of a criminal offence, removed from a Performers List or declared bankrupt.
- The PCT is concerned about patient safety.
- The PCT considers that the Contractor's financial situation places the PCT at risk of material financial loss.

Not all of these are necessarily automatic. The PCT has some discretion in those cases where they believe that the person in question has not been rendered unsuitable to be a Contractor because of a criminal conviction or disqualification or suspension imposed by a body outside the UK.

In accordance with Clause 335 of the standard dental contract, the PCT will only exercise its right to terminate the contract if it is satisfied that, in its view, the cumulative effect of the breaches has adversely affected the services provided under the contract.

However, it is important for Performers and indeed other staff members to recognise that a GDS Contract can be terminated, and they may lose their job, in circumstances over which they have no control.

When a Contractor dies, their spouse can also be in a vulnerable position. They have seven days in which to inform the PCT of the Contractor's death, otherwise the contract will terminate automatically. Even then, the maximum time a spouse of a deceased Contractor has to dispose of the practice is six months.

▶ p 158. In certain circumstances a Contractor can appeal to the National Health Service Litigation Authority. As a public body the decisions the PCT make are subject to appeal through the Administrative courts if the PCT has either exceeded or abused its legal powers or failed to follow the appropriate procedures.

Consequences of termination

On termination of the contract for whatever reason, the Contractor has to:

- co-operate with the PCT to enable any outstanding matters to be dealt with

- co-operate with the PCT to arrange for patients to be transferred on to one or more Contractors (for the purposes of the contract it is only those patients who are under an open course of treatment that would need to be transferred)
- provide 'reasonable information about individual patients to such other appropriate person the PCT specifies'.

At the end the PCT will make a reconciliation of payments made and received by the Contractor within three months. Even if more UDAs pro rata are completed the PCT is still obliged to pay for these subject to the maximum annual UDA numbers.

NHS dispute procedure

In the case of any dispute arising out of or in connection with the contract, the Contractor and the PCT must make every reasonable effort to communicate and co-operate with each other with a view to resolving the dispute, before referring the dispute for determination. Contractual disputes can be resolved easily if both parties take a pragmatic approach to problem-solving and communicate early and effectively with each other. As with other aspects of the contract, it is crucial that you keep comprehensive records: in the event of a dispute about any aspect of the contract, you should note down any verbal and written communications you have with PCT managers to ensure that an audit trail is available.

The NHS dispute procedure can be used to resolve any dispute arising out of or in connection with the contract including in relation to its termination. The important points are:

R NHS (General Dental Services Contracts) 2006 S3 P7 ¶55–7 (page 41).

- A written notice of the dispute is sent to the NHSLA.
- Time limits are within three years of the date on which the matter giving rise to the dispute occurred or should have reasonably come to the attention of the party bringing the dispute.
- The statement should be a factual account of the matter in dispute, with the relevant regulations quoted which you believe have been breached by the other party.
- Observations are invited by the Secretary of State within seven days of receiving the dispute notice and all parties can make representations.
- The Secretary of State notifies the parties who are appointed to hear the dispute and oral representations can be made.
- The whole process should take between two and four weeks, but this can be extended by the Secretary of State if there is good reason.

NHS Litigation Authority

The NHS Litigation Authority (NHSLA) was established on 20 November 1995 to indemnify English NHS bodies against claims for clinical negligence. The NHSLA is a Special Health Authority and, therefore, part of the National Health Service. It is not an insurance company.

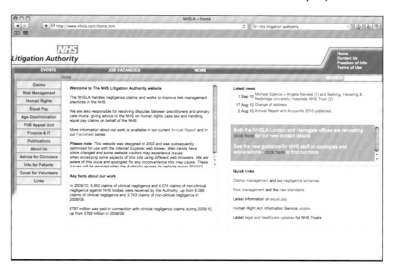

Figure 21: NHS Litigation Authority website (www.nhsla.com).

From 1 April 1999 the NHSLA's responsibilities were expanded to include non-clinical claims under the Liabilities to Third Parties Scheme (LTPS) and Property Expenses Scheme (PES). More recently, the Authority has acquired further, more diverse, functions: the provision of an information service to the NHS on the impact of the Human Rights Act 1998 (from January 2003), the functions of the former SHA, the Family Health Services Appeal Authority (from April 2005), and the provision of advice about and assistance with litigation on equal pay claims (from August 2005).

From 2005 the FHS Appeals Unit of the NHSLA integrated the new dental dispute resolution procedures into its caseload, to achieve determinations for dentists and PCTs in dispute both for pre-contract disputes as well as ongoing disputes, particularly those relating to underperformance and claw-back of funding.

The NHSLA has been involved in resolving several pre-contract disputes and its anonymised reports are available on its website. The following are some of the decisions that have been made:

- The PCT has a discretion to make amendments to the contract value if there were changes in the number of dentists or activity after the test period, but there is no compulsion on the PCT to exercise this discretion. The PCT's only obligation was to offer a contract based on the activity in the test period according to the Statement of Financial Entitlement guidance.

- Dentists are expected to undertake continuing professional development (CPD) and clinical audit in line with the PCT's clinical governance framework. There is no loss of income associated with this and therefore no compensatory payments.

- A practice cannot provide treatment or urgent treatment on a limited basis only (i.e. one day a week), as this is an inferior service. It must provide its NHS services during the same hours as it did in March 2006, just prior to the start of the new contract.

- In a growing practice, especially an orthodontic practice, the PCT is not obliged to commit to the same level of future activity. The decision should be a local one based on needs assessment and an oral health strategy. It is for the PCT to form a local view on the level of activity commissioned from dentists, in line with affordability and the local population's needs.

- Contracts between Contractors and PCTs are personal to the parties and cannot be assigned to a successor Contractor who is not party to the agreement. There is no right under the Regulations for the Contractor to be able to give, sell, assign or otherwise dispose of the benefits of any rights under the agreement. This clearly has implications for the sale of practices and goodwill.

- PCTs have the ability to commission services for defined groups (for example children) where they consider that it is appropriate to do so and can justify this decision in terms of local need.

- There is no compulsion on a PCT to commission more growth from a particular practice.

Underperformance

A PCT has the discretion to grant an amnesty where a Contractor has underperformed on a contract. However, there is no legal compulsion on them to do so. In one case, after a family bereavement, the PCT was said to have acted reasonably in giving the Contractor four months within which to pay back most, but not all, of the unperformed amount.

NHSLA Ref 14128.

NHS Body status

At the start of a contract Contractors can elect to become Health Service bodies. Contractors are advised not to do this as being a Health Service body deprives you of the flexibility of challenging the PCT in a civil claim in the event of a dispute. If you are not a Health Service body you are not obliged to accept the NHS dispute resolution machinery if you do not want to. If the Contractor agrees in writing to use the dispute procedure then the PCT has to agree.

The Appeal Court

Crouch v South Birmingham Primary Care Trust.

In February 2008 Eddie Crouch, an orthodontist working in South Birmingham PCT, having unsuccessfully appealed to the Chief Officer of the Family Health Service Appeal Unit (FHSAU), took his judicial review of this decision on to the High Court in London. Two issues were put before Mr Justice Collins, the Appeal Court judge:

1) South Birmingham PCT should have carried out a needs assessment prior to the introduction of the new contract in April 2006 in accordance with Section 11 of the Health and Social Care Act 2001.

2) The PCT should not be allowed to insert into his PDS contract a clause allowing them to terminate his contract at any time and without cause.

Mr Justice Collins was particularly scathing about NHS regulations for dentists, comparing the process to

> **going through a marsh, trying to leap from tussock to tussock. I do pity those poor dentists who have to struggle with this kind of rubbish.**

'Dentist close to winning High Court battle over contract'. *Birmingham Post*, February 26 2008.

Eddie Crouch lost his first point about the requirement for the PCT to consult with the local population but Mr Justice Collins upheld his appeal on the second point. It was confirmed that it was not open to the PCT to include a provision in his PDS contract that would allow it to terminate the PDS contracts at any time without cause by written notice.

Part 3 para 66–69 of the Regulations clearly provides the circumstances and manner in which a PDS Agreement had to be terminated in accordance with the Regulations. Unless an orthodontist breached a PDS Agreement or one of the proscribed grounds for termination arose, a PCT could not terminate a PDS contracts except on the date that the contract provided for.

A PDS Agreement was intended to last five years. This was clearly good news for all orthodontists, since they are the main holders of PDS Agreements. However, following the handing down of the judgement the Secretary of State, as advised by the Department of Health, decided to appeal this judgement and was given leave to appeal by the Courts.

Crouch R (on the application of) v Secretary of State for Health [2008] EWCA Civ 1365.

The case was heard on 27 November 2008 in the Court of Appeal before the Master of the Rolls, Lord Justice Dyson and Lord Justice Jackson. All three judges rejected the Department of Health's arguments, pointing out that if it was the intention of the regulations to allow PCTs to terminate PDS contracts, express powers allowing this would have been included in those regulations. In the end they attributed part of the confusion to the inadequate drafting of the PDS regulations but concluded that if the PCT was allowed to terminate the contract at any time without cause, even where the Contractor's performance was beyond criticism, the Contractor would be worse off than if he did breach the contract.

Performance issues

Where there is no identifiable breach of GDS/PDS regulations some PCTs are using the NHS Performers List regulations to manage particular situations. These may not always be the appropriate method to deal with issues that are raised and it is important to understand clearly how the regulations were intended to work.

Disciplinary proceedings should not be used to punish genuine mistakes or conscientiously taken decisions which might, with the benefit of hindsight, have been different. A practitioner's willingness to co-operate with locally developed measures to help them improve their performance, along with their co-operation with and response to independent review, are likely to be important factors in reaching a decision. Disciplinary proceedings should be seen as the last resort locally where other actions have proved unsuccessful in the past or seem unlikely to be productive.

Contractors will be subject to GDS regulations and the civil contract they have with the PCT. Sometimes problems occur as a result of a Performer's clinical treatments, behaviour and attitude, prescribing and claiming profiles and management of complaints. Contractors will remain responsible for the actions of their Performers under the contract and will therefore have to deal with any issues arising out of their obligation set out in the standard contract.

Performers List regulations

Where there are concerns about clinical behaviour, PCTs are advised that it might be better to use the Performers List regulations to remove the dentist from the Performers List, rather than handle the issue under the GDS Regulations. Using this route, the dentist could ultimately be debarred from practising on the NHS.

Handling performance issues in NHS Dentistry Contracts. V1.0, July 2007. (Primary Care Contracting)

If the Performer happens to be the Contractor, the contract will automatically be terminated if they are subject to national disqualification. As a result the practice may well be closed if the PCT does not allow the contract to be transferred to another Contractor or Performer.

Although a dentist must be on a Performers List in order to practice dentistry on the NHS, it does not necessarily have to be in the same area that the dentist is working in – this enables locums to move around the country – but should in normal circumstances be the list of the area in which the majority of the dentist's NHS clinical time is spent.

Using the Performers List Regulations, the PCT can do the following:

1) *Mandatorily remove the dentist from the Performers List.*
    A PCT must remove a dentist from the dental Performers List if he or she:

    - is convicted in the UK of murder
    - is convicted in the UK of a criminal offence and has been sentenced to serve a prison term of more than 6 months
    - is subject to a national disqualification
    - has died
    - is included in the dental Performers List of another PCT
    - is no longer a dentist (i.e. is no longer on the GDC Register)
    - is the subject of a determination by the Professional Conduct Committee to suspend him under Section 27 of the Dentist Act (erasure or suspension)
    - is the subject of a direction of a Practice Committee of the GDC
    - has failed to complete vocational training and has not withdrawn from the list.

2) *Remove the dentist from the list on a discretionary basis.*
    There are four grounds for discretionary removal:

    - unsuitability
    - involvement in fraud related to a health scheme
    - inefficiency
    - inability to show that they have been working as a dentist in the PCT's area in the preceding 12 months.

In order to reduce the PCTs' administrative burden it is considered entirely reasonable for a PCT to remove from its list any Performers who are no longer performing services within its area.

3) *Contingently remove the dentist from the list.*
    In a contingent removal case the Performer remains on the list conditional on them agreeing to certain conditions imposed on them by the PCT to remove any prejudice to the efficiency of the service or to prevent further acts or omissions in a fraud case.

4) *Conditionally include a dentist on a Performers List.*
    A dentist will be able to practice as long as they comply with the conditions, which could mean:

    - a restriction on where they practise
    - a restriction on the type of treatment they carry out
    - an agreement to carry out further education and training.

    The dentist can appeal these conditions to the Primary Health Lists jurisdiction.

5) *Suspend a dentist.*

Suspension is intended to be a neutral act and not a disciplinary action. It is intended to protect the interests of patients, staff and the dentist who is suspended and should not be used without reasonable justification. In exercising their power under Regulation 13 of the NHS Performers List, the PCT must be satisfied 'that it is necessary to do so for the protection of members of the public or is otherwise in the public interest'.

Conditions regarding suspension

There are provisions for payment of a suspended dentist which are covered by regulations.

The PCT can suspend a dentist for up to six months but can ask the Primary Health Lists jurisdiction to increase this time. PCTs usually use the suspension process while they consider whether to remove (or contingently remove) a dentist from a list or while they are awaiting a decision affecting the dentist, whether from a court anywhere in the world or from a licensing or regulatory body like the GDC. The dentist has no right of appeal against the decision to suspend. They can, however, ask for a review in cases where they have been suspended while awaiting the outcome of a criminal prosecution or where the PCT has imposed altered requirements under the criteria for conditional inclusion or contingent removal.

Primary Health Lists

Until 18 January 2010 appeals and applications were heard by the Family Health Services Appeal Authority. This role has now been taken over by the Primary Health Lists jurisdiction. This is within the Health, Education and Social Care Chamber of the First Tier Tribunal. The Primary Health Lists system is under the supervision of the Health, Education and Social Care Chamber President. It is independent of the Department of Health and is not accountable to the Health Secretary. Appeals and applications are made directly to it.

The procedural rules governing the appeal process are statutorily defined in The Family Health Services Appeals Authority (Procedure) Rules 2001 www.opsi.gov.uk/si/si2001/20013750.htm

The President, who is appointed by the Lord Chancellor, allocates appeals and applications to panels normally consisting of a legal chairman, a professional member and a lay member. The panels will hold oral hearings into the matters referred to them unless the Appellant or Applicant says that they do not want one.

NHS Performers List – England and Wales. BDA Advice Note 82, August 2006.

A Performer can appeal to the Primary Health Lists against the following decisions by a PCT:

- refusing admission to a Performers List
- imposing (or amending) certain conditions under 'conditional inclusion'

- removing a Performer from its list because they:
  - have not complied with a condition imposed under conditional inclusion
  - have not complied with a condition imposed under conditional removal
  - are an 'efficiency case' or an unsuitability case, or are involved in a fraud case.

Any party to the proceedings has a right of appeal under and by virtue of Section 11 of the Tribunals and Inquiries Act 1992 by lodging notice in the Royal Courts of Justice within 28 days. The grounds for judicial review are very limited and can only involve cases where the procedure has not been followed by the Authority. This area of public law is very specialised and would require the input of a solicitor and barrister.

Examples of recent appeal cases

As these cases occurred prior to January 2010, they were dealt with by the Family Health Services Appeal Authority.

- **13122. Refusal to join Dental List.**
  The applicant was a Spanish dentist who applied to join a Dental List. Questions as to the authenticity of references provided in support of the application were raised. Doubts remained following investigation by the Local Counter Fraud Specialist who concluded that three of the references contained exactly the same wording, the header on the references appeared to have been downloaded or copied from the University of Madrid and two references were from the same person but with a different signature. In addition, none of the documents describing themselves as references spoke of clinical practice in two recent posts which lasted at least three months. There was no explanation and alternative referee.
  Appeal refused.

- **12333/4. Appeal by Dental Practitioner against refusal to join Dental List.**
  The Practitioner commenced work the day after making an application to join a List but before the application was granted. She became caught up in investigations concerning the practice. Both she and the agency through which she obtained employment were genuinely unaware of the breach of regulations and she stopped work as soon as the breach was pointed out. The refusal was based on inefficiency and unsuitability. On the basis that the Practitioner had been accepted onto another List the PCT barely resisted the appeal. The Panel found the breach of regulations technical with no intention to deceive: it did not, by itself, make the Practitioner unsuitable. There was no evidence of inefficiency.
  Appeal allowed.

If a dentist finds themselves in any situation that poses a potential risk to their Performers List number it is important they seek early advice from their defence organisation.

Actions by the Contractor

Termination notice by the Contractor

The Contractor can terminate their notice by giving three months' written notice to the PCT. This three months' notice ends on the last day of the month in which the termination date falls. In other words, if notice is deemed to have been received on 5 July, the contract will terminate on 31 October – that is, closer to four months than three.

Clause 310, standard contract.

The Contractor will be expected to co-operate with the PCT to enable patients to be transferred to other Contractors and to provide reasonable information about individual patients to any appropriate person the PCT specifies. For the purposes of the contract a patient is defined as a person to whom the Contractor is providing services under the contract. This means if the patient is not currently under a course of treatment the Contractor is under no obligation to give information about the practice list or the database of patients it has seen to the PCT.

A practice considering giving up its contract should ensure that it has achieved its pro-rata UDA target by the end of the notice period, otherwise the PCT is entitled to recover the money. There are no provisos for the Contractor to contact patients or make any other arrangements. However, if a practice is closing down, or the owner retiring or selling, a practitioner may wish to contact patients and inform them of the change in circumstances simply as a matter of courtesy.

Change in status

Partnerships

Minor changes to contracts with an individual Contractor or two or more individuals practising in partnership are dealt with the GDS Regulations.

R *NHS (General Dental Service Contracts) 2005 S3 P9 ¶62.*

The contract stipulates that where an individual dentist proposes to practise in partnership with one or more partners, they need to inform the PCT in writing, giving them:

- the name of the partners
- the date on which the partnership arrangement come into force which must not be less than 28 days from the letter informing the PCT of the change
- confirmation that they are a dentist or a registered DCP.

There must also be in existence a partnership deed which needs to be disclosed to the PCT.

The advice to PCTs is that such partnership changes do not necessarily mean the contract has to be terminated and should be dealt with simply as contract variations, subject to satisfactory information being provided to the PCT. The same is not true of incorporation (see 'Body corporate' below) which is not considered a 'minor change' in this context.

The partnership route is advocated by a number of specialist law firms as a means of protecting the practice goodwill upon the sale of the practice. The contract is a personal contract between the Contractor and the PCT and therefore cannot be part of a sale of a practice without permission of the PCT who is commissioning that service. The suggestion from lawyers is that taking the potential purchaser of the practice into a partnership, whose identity is confirmed to the PCT, and then allowing the vendor to retire at a later date, theoretically protects the goodwill of the practice, since the PCT will not be entitled to renegotiate the contract simply because a partner has changed.

Without this, when a practice owner sells the practice, the NHS contract will have to be terminated and it will be at the PCT's discretion whether they issue a new contract on the same terms and conditions to the purchaser of the practice, whether they vary it or whether they issue one at all.

Body corporate

If the practice becomes a Dental Body Corporate (DBC) – either as a private company limited by shares or a Limited Liability Partnership – then a new GDS Contract is required. This contract includes the specific provisions relating to DBCs as well as the new signatories. It follows, therefore, that the previous contract or agreement held by the practice will terminate by virtue of incorporation. In its guidance the PCC says that in most cases this will be a straightforward like-for-like contract transfer but this gives the PCT an opportunity to renegotiate the terms of a new contract if it wishes to do so.

Briefing paper: termination of dental contracts and sale of goodwill August 2006 Primary Care Contracting.

'The Contractor shall not give, sell, assign or otherwise dispose of the benefit of any rights under this contract, save in accordance with the contract.' Model General Dental Services Contract part 2 Clause 12.

Briefing paper: termination of dental contracts and sale of goodwill. August 2006. (Primary Care Contracting)

14 COMPLAINTS PROCEDURE

Most businesses accept as only human nature the fact that things do not always work out perfectly and that inevitably this generates complaints from time to time. These organisations recognise the importance of the complaints and the opportunity they offer in improving the future service that business delivers. In a sense complaints are free market research on your performance and systems. Dentists tend to be less pragmatic than this and feel threatened by complaints, often considering them a personal attack on their professional integrity and using their complaints procedure reactively rather than proactively.

What the patient did next. Dental Protection Annual Review 2006.

For an increasing number of dentists the complaint they received most recently was the first they had received for many years, if ever. This makes it all the more difficult to cope with and reflects the increasingly consumerist nature of society and the supermarket-style 'no quibbles' guarantee expected to be thrown in with every course of treatment.

D'Cruz (2007).

Schedule 3 Part 6 of the Regulations sets out provisions for dealing with complaints. This largely mirrors the old GDS system, with a duty to set up a complaints procedure with a named contact and an obligation to deal with complaints. The requirement for you to co-operate with any investigation comes about through Section 17 of the 1977 National Health Service Act which existed under Paragraphs 31A and 31B of Schedule 1 to the GDS Regulations (S I 1992/661).

A definition of complaints is not provided by regulations; however, a working description is 'an expression of dissatisfaction with the practice's procedures, charges, personnel or quality of service'. Recent research indicates that while very few people actually complain, a higher number are dissatisfied with certain aspects of their care but either did not know whom to complain to or how to go about it.

Rattan (2004).

Bedi *et al.* (2005).

Complaints occur when precipitating factors and predisposing factors occur simultaneously.

Precipitating factors are those that actually give rise to the complaint, such as an adverse outcome, providing incorrect care and system errors and mistakes. This could range from the laboratory work not being delivered in time for a patient's appointment to an anaphylactic reaction to the administration of a local anaesthetic.

A *predisposing factor* on its own does not result in a complaint but increases the chance of it, such as rudeness, delays, lack of attention, apathy or poor communication. It is when the precipitating factors are overlaid with the predisposing factors that a patient can direct the blame at a series of individuals and a complaint crystallizes.

D'Cruz (2008).

Why patients complain

The NHS provides about 380 million treatments every year. While only about one in every 4,000 of these treatments result in a formal complaint, that equates to approximately 100,000 complaints a year.

Berry (2007).

So why do patients complain? What actually motivates them to put pen to paper or pick up the phone or speak to a receptionist or manager or indeed other third parties? Contrary to a deeply held suspicion it is not those who are awkward and difficult that are the most likely to complain and complaints are seldom vexatious or mischievous. In every complaint there is always something that can be learnt, even if it is simply the manner in which something is said or done.

Setting up and running in-house complaints procedures. Dental Protection Risk Management Pack.

The most common reasons for making a complaint are:

- an outlet
- an apology
- an explanation
- appropriate remedial action
- redress/recompense/refund.

Other sources of information cite other different reasons for complaining. The top five issues raised in complaints against dental practices as reported by the Healthcare Commission in 2002 are:

Spotlight on Complaints. Healthcare Commission Annual Report, January 2002.

1) quality of care
2) cost of treatment or challenge in the way in which costs are determined
3) removal of patients from practice list
4) poor communication with patients
5) problems with availability of dentists in the NHS.

▶ p 180.
Dental Complaints Service Press release. 5 October 2006.

The Dental Complaints Service has identified the top five areas of complaints (in order of frequency) for both treatment and service issues:

- Treatment issues –
  - restorations (amalgam and tooth coloured)
  - dentures
  - crowns
  - bridges

- ▨ root canal treatments.
- ◉ Service issues –
  - ▨ pain
  - ▨ cost
  - ▨ rudeness
  - ▨ access to treatment
  - ▨ consent.

As far as the Dental Complaints Service complaints were concerned issues of 'pain' or 'cost' were cited in 83 per cent of complaints received, though fewer than 40 per cent of complainants appeared to want their money back. The pattern is similar and reflects the subjective nature of the relationship between patients and dentists, mediated by expectations of a particular type and level of service, and linked in some cases with the method of payment for dental services.

While there is a general feeling that complaints are on the increase, a survey by the Office of Fair Trading in 2003 indicated that only 6 per cent of patients have ever felt they had cause to complain. Of that 6 per cent, only 3 per cent actually did complain.

Survey of consumers' experience of dental services. Office of Fair Trading, March 2003 www.oft.gov.uk/shared_oft/reports/ consumer_protection/oft630b.pdf.

Specific NHS complaints that are made to the PCT or the Patient Advice and Liaison Services (PALS) include lack of information about costs, difficulty in accessing services or particular types of treatments such as endodontics, and misleading information about mixing NHS and private treatment.

▶ p 174.

When a practice set up a complaints procedure it must specify a **complaints manager** who will be responsible for receiving and investigating all complaints which can be made or recorded in writing. The complaint has to be acknowledged within three working days, with a substantive response following an investigation within a time limit agreed with the complainant and giving a written summary of the investigation and its conclusions. There is a contractual obligation to make patients aware about the complaints procedures as well as the role of other bodies – such as the PCT – in relation to complaints and also to advise them of their right to assistance with their complaint from independent advocacy services.

The practice must keep a record of all complaints and copies of all correspondence relating to complaints for a period of at least two years from the date on which the complaints were made. However, such complaint records must be kept separate from the patient dental records. There is a further requirement to make an annual return to the PCT, stating the number of complaints received in the previous year.

The NHS complaints procedure

The legal framework for the current NHS complaints procedure is set out in the National Health Service (Complaints) Regulations 2009. The regulations cover the fundamental requirements of good complaints handling, but not the processes through which outcomes are to be delivered. This will be determined locally by the PCT.

Reform of health and social care complaints – proposed changes to the legislative framework. December 2008 (GR 10956). Department of Health.

The complaints procedure has seen significant changes over the past decade or so. Since 1996 the procedure has separated complaints from discipline and created a two-stage process, starting with local resolution by the body or person complained about. If that did not resolve the issue the case may have been referred to an independent panel. Since 1996 the complaints system has been unified so that the same complaints system covers hospitals, community and primary care services (family doctors, dentists, opticians and pharmacists) and can handle concerns about both administration and clinical treatment.

NHS Complaints Procedure National Evaluation. York Health Economics Consortium and System Three Social Research, March 2001.

A review of the complaints procedure was undertaken in 1999/2000 and in September 2001 the Department of Health issued *Reforming the NHS Complaints Procedure – A Listening Document* which sought comments on the evaluation report. It was not until March 2003 that the Department of Health published *NHS Complaints Reform – Making Things Right*. This set out a programme to improve the management of the whole complaints system and identified the need for effective links to wider systems around quality such as clinical governance, patient safety and staff training in complaints. Patients are supported through PALS and ICAS (Independent Complaints Advocacy Services).

Much of what has happened in the arena of complaints management has been driven by several high-profile medical cases and their subsequent inquiries. These include the Bristol Inquiry into children's heart surgery, the Richard Neale and Clifford Ayling Inquiries in September 2004 as well as those into William Kerr and Michael Haslam. Although each of these has its particular features, there is a common thread running through all four enquiries: the failure of those in positions of authority in the NHS or in the regulators to detect signs of unacceptable or incompetent professional behaviour and to take effective action to protect patients.

Making Experiences Count. June 2007 (GR 8288). Department of Health.

The background to the latest changes in complaints handling in April 2009 is the unification of health services and social services. This reflects the fact that many people use services that cross health and social care boundaries.

What existed up until April 2009 was a three-stage process:

1) local resolution
2) Healthcare Commission independent review
3) Health Service Ombudsman

The process is now in two stages (also referred to as 'tiers' or 'levels'). The second stage above, the Healthcare Commission review, has been removed. In 2005 the Health Service Ombudsman identified significant weakness and failings in the system. These included:

- it was not centred on the patient's needs
- it was fragmented across different services.

Making things better? A report on reform of the NHS complaints procedure in England. Parliamentary and Health Service Ombudsman, 2nd Report, 2004/5.

It was also clear that the involvement of the Healthcare Commission in the second stage of this process led the emphasis away from local resolution, as PCTs would rely on the Healthcare Commission to carry out any investigations. Eight thousand requests for independent review were lodged every year with the Healthcare Commission. In 33 per cent of cases it was found that the healthcare Provider could have done more to resolve the complaint. In the Healthcare Commission's opinion relatively straightforward measures would often have provided the solution: in 85 per cent of cases, referring back to the Provider for further action appeared to have been successful. From the dental practice's perspective this gave the complainant a chance to 'have another go'; the Healthcare Commission would often start a completely new investigation, with all its attendant paperwork and time commitment. The prevailing wisdom is that if complaints are properly handled and responded to at a local level, with appropriate accountability, there should be no need to have the second layer of complaints management.

Spotlight on Complaints. Healthcare Commission Annual Report, January 2002.

A number of Early Adopter sites piloted the new two-tier proposals from August 2008 onwards to share good practice and develop toolkits on PALS customer care and managing persistent or unreasonable complainants.

Managingyourorganisation/
Legalandcontractual/Complaintspolicy/
MakingExperiencesCount/Earlyadopters/
index.htm.

The aims of the new changes are:

- to ensure the process is focused on outcomes with swift local resolution
- to put the patient at the centre of the process to allow increased access and uptake
- to ensure the practice learns from individual complaints and that those lessons lead to service improvement.

Level One: Local resolution (practice)

Local resolution is the first part of the new two-stage process that is common to all parts of the NHS and social care. The intention is to make this part of the process responsive enough to deal with the majority of the complaints received by general dental practitioners, the aim being that the practice itself deals with the problem quickly and efficiently.

● What can patients complain about?

- Any matter that is reasonably connected with the practice (which can be a very wide range of issues).

● What can patients NOT complain about?

  ● Complaints that have already been investigated under the complaints regulations.

  ● Complaints arising out of the alleged failure to comply with a data subject request under the Data Protection Act 1998.

  ● Complaints arising out of an alleged failure by the practice to comply with a request for information under the Freedom of Information Act 2000.

Complaints procedure

Complaints can be made verbally to front line staff or to clinical staff. They may be dealt with without having to go through a more formal process if the complainant is satisfied. If the complainant is not satisfied with the response, they can make a more formal complaint to be dealt with more extensively.

A patient wishing to make a complaint can complain directly to the practice or to the PCT in writing, by e-mail or by telephone. If the practice receives the complaint within three days it must:

  ● acknowledge the complaint and offer the opportunity to discuss either by telephone or face to face how the complaint is to be handled

  ● copy the complaints correspondence to the PCT.

If the PCT receives the complaint they will work with the complainant to determine how to handle the case. Decisions will be taken on an individual basis and will depend on the facts as known at the time. Simple complaints may be referred back to the practice, but where there are clinical issues or safety issues the PCT may want to handle and investigate the complaint itself.

When the PCT receives the initial complaint it will check with the practice to see if a complaint has also been lodged there. If so, the PCT will have to discuss how the complaint is to be handled; in any case, the PCT will retain an overview of how the complaint is handled.

If a complaint lodged with the practice is not resolved locally, the complainant cannot then refer it to the PCT, although it can still be referred to the Health Service Ombudsman.

Who can make a complaint?

A complaint can be made by a service used or any person affected by or likely to be affected by the action, omission or decision of the practice. Someone acting on behalf of another person may make a complaint on behalf of that person, where that person is unable to make the complaint themselves or has asked the person to make the complaint on their behalf. In the context of clinical treatment and disclosure of confidential patient information, if the complainant is not the patient consent may need to be provided by the patient to act on their behalf.

Time limits

A complaint must be made within 12 months from the date on which the matter occurred or came to the notice of the complainant. While these are the regulations there is further provision to waive these limits where there are good reasons to do so and it is still possible to investigate the case effectively. The response times for general dental practices are an acknowledgement within three days.

The proposal is that there are no fixed time limits for the substantive response, as this should be agreed with the complainant. In complex cases involving different practitioners, treatment over a long period of time or other services such as secondary care centres, the intention is that a full investigation can be carried out, unencumbered by rigid and artificial time constraints, so that the complainant has a full response and the organisation itself is able to learn from the lessons. It also enables the respondents to obtain their own independent advice from their indemnity organisations. It is generally accepted that the longer the delay in responding the more entrenched both parties may become, unless there is agreement from the complainant about the timescales for response.

Performance measurements targets will be set to look at what percentage of complaints were dealt with within certain times rather than focusing on how long individual complaints took to be responded to or resolved. In other words, there will be a focus on outcomes rather than process.

Complaints can of course be brought at any time in relation to private treatment, though civil claims in negligence have their own time limits dictated by statute (The Limitation Act, 1980). The intention of local resolution is to involve the complainants throughout the local process so their views can be taken into account. It is hoped that this will make the investigation more robust and proportionate, particularly as the complainant will be given a full report of the investigations.

Common problems identified in the way complaints have been handled at a local level include:

Spotlight on complaints.
Healthcare Commission, 2006.

- failure to acknowledge that a complaint is valid
- failure to apologise, even where local shortcomings are identified
- responses which do not explain what steps have been taken to prevent the recurrence of the event which has given rise to the complaint
- responses which contain technical or dental terms, which the complainant may not understand
- failure to involve staff directly concerned in the complaint during the local investigation.

What is also important as part of local resolutions are the lessons the practice may learn from the complaint and the changes it intends to make as a result. The cultural shift here is to move away from the adversarial system of responding to complaints to an emphasis towards preventing harm, reducing risks and learning from complaints.

The model envisaged for effective complaints handling should be based on facilitating quality outcomes in terms of patients' satisfaction and learning:

Figure 22: Model for effective complaints handling.

Complaints Manager

The role of the complaints manager assumes greater importance in the new system. All complaints must have 'organisational sign off' when the complaints has been concluded at the first level. Responsibility for this sign off needs to be given to someone who would be accountable for the operation of the complaints arrangements within the organisation. They need to be senior enough in the organisation to be able to ensure the following:

- identifying the need for, and influencing, organisational change in response to any complaints
- giving complainants the confidence that the complaint is being dealt with appropriately.

In general dental practice the person with the most senior authority is likely to be the practice owner or one of the partners.

A 'sign off letter' should be sent to the complainant. The letter will:

- confirm the practice is satisfied with the way that the complaint has been addressed and the action taken
- make clear to the complainant that all appropriate action has been taken at local level
- inform the complainant of their right to take the case to the Ombudsman if they remain dissatisfied.

Within that sign off letter there must be a written explanation of:

- how the complaint was considered
- the conclusions reached on the basis of the facts
- an explanation of what action if any the practice intends to take as a consequence.

Annual report to PCT

All NHS dental practices will need to send an annual report to the PCT containing details of:

- how many complaints have been received
- a summary of the subject matter
- whether they were upheld or not
- whether there is a record of them having been referred to the Ombudsman
- a narrative drawing on significant issues from the practice's handling of complaints throughout the year including lessons learned and actions taken.

Level One: Local resolution (PCT)

Role of the PCT

The role of the PCT in local resolution will be two-fold:

1) investigation of complaints where appropriate
2) monitoring dental practices' complaints handling performance.

Complaints investigation

Much of the complaints investigation infrastructure, including the PCT's access to experienced personnel, has been dismantled over the last decade; it is likely that the management of complaints will depend very much on local circumstances. The very flexibility of the system may make it more unwieldy and difficult for both complainants and practices to manage.

As part of the local resolution stage, conciliation could be offered where, following an investigation, an immediate oral response seems inappropriate or where the complainant remains dissatisfied following an earlier response. Conciliation is used when a person wishes to complain under a practice-based procedure, and it would, in the opinion of the PCT, be unreasonable to expect the complaint to be made directly to the dentist concerned, or where the complainant is dissatisfied with the investigation carried out in the practice-based procedure. PALS and ICAS will be an integral part of the local resolution machinery.

▶ pp 177–8.

Monitoring complaints handling performance

Practices will need to monitor their own responsiveness to complaints so that patients are satisfied with the resolution of complaints they raise and practices can demonstrate that they have taken account of the issues and incorporated changes where appropriate.

PCTs will be responsible for the external monitoring of complaints handling and responsiveness. Using the contract, PCT will set out specific requirements on responding to complaints and will require information from Providers on complaints received and how they have responded to them. This information will form part of an overall picture of the practice's effectiveness as a Provider of services and will inform subsequent commissioning decisions.

Making Experiences Count (MEC) Complaints Toolkit – Draft v1. Department of Health, 2008.

In order to assess the importance or significance of a complaint PCTs will look at a risk management matrix which looks at the consequences of a complaint and then assess the likelihood of a recurrence of the incidents that gave rise to the complaints.

An anonymised version of the reports sent by practices to the PCT will need to be made available to the local population, with information about any lessons learned from the complaints received.

Consequence Categorisation Table

The following table assists in determining how to categorise the consequences of a complaint, or the subject matter of a complaint.

Table 12: Consequence categorisation.

Category	Description
Serious	Issues regarding serious adverse events, long-term damage, grossly substandard care, professional misconduct or death that require investigation. Serious safety issues. Probability of litigation high.
Major	Significant issues of standards, quality of care, or denial of rights. Complaints with clear quality assurance or risk management implications or issues causing lasting detriment that require investigation. Possibility of litigation.
Moderate	Potential to impact on service provision/delivery. Legitimate consumer concern but not causing lasting detriment. Slight potential for litigation.
Minor	Minimal impact and relative minimal risk to the provision of care or the service. No real risk of litigation
Minimum	No impact or risk to provision of care.

14: Complaints procedure

Likelihood Categorisation Table

The following table assists in determining the likelihood of recurrence of the incident or circumstances giving rise to the complaint.

Table 13: Likelihood categorisation.

Likelihood	Description
Frequent	Recurring found or experienced often
Probable	Will probably occur several times a year
Occasional	Happening from time to time – not constant, irregular
Uncommon	Rare – unusual but may have happened before
Remote	Isolated or 'one off' – slight/vague connection to service provision

Table 14: Risk Assessment Matrix (Complaints).

Having assessed the consequence and likelihood categories using the tables above, the risk assessment matrix below can be used to determine the level of risk that should be assigned to the complaint.

Consequence	Likelihood of recurrence				
	high	probable	occasional	uncommon	remote
serious	**HIGH**				
major					
moderate			**MEDIUM**		
minor					
minimum					**LOW**

Patient Advice and Liaison Services

The **Patient Advice and Liaison Services** (PALS) were set up in the NHS in 2002. Their core function is to provide confidential advice and support to patients to resolve concerns quickly. PALS are locally based in PCTs and often act to provide information to dental patients concerned about charges, availability of services and provision of dental care. They also monitor trends and gaps in services and report these to the trust management for action. They also liaise with contracts managers to report difficulties with certain practices and provide the 'soft' intelligence about how practices are managing the contract from the patients' perspective. They are useful in negotiating speedy solutions to problems and preventing them escalating simply by providing appropriate information or liaising between the practice and the patient.

Independent Complaints Advocacy Service (ICAS)

Section 12 of the Social and Health Care Act 2001 places a duty on the Secretary of State for Health to make arrangements to provide an **Independent Complaints Advocacy Service** to assist individuals in making complaints against the NHS. ICAS was established to support patients and members of the public wishing to make a complaint about their NHS care or treatment. This statutory national service was launched in September 2003 and is delivered to agreed quality standards. It is patient-centred, delivering support ranging from provision of self help information to the assignment of a dedicated advocate to assist individuals with letter writing, form filling and attendance at meetings. Their one-to-one generic advocacy services operates as POhWER.

Care Quality Commission

▶ p 21.

The establishment of this organisation to replace the Healthcare Commission has been described in the 'Arm's length bodies' section of Chapter 3. The Care Quality Commission will be registering practices and will require practices to ensure complaints are responded to effectively.

Standards for Better Health Department of Health 2004.

NHS Standards for Better Health under the Patient Focus Domain requires practices to have systems in place to ensure that patients:

- have suitable and accessible information about, and clear access to, procedures to register formal complaints and feedback on the quality of services
- are not discriminated against when complaints are made
- are assured that organisations act appropriately on any concerns and, where appropriate, make changes to ensure improvements in service delivery.

As part of its inspection function the Care Quality Commission will be looking at:

- accessibility
- integration
- resources
- governance and management.

The CQC will be looking at outcomes of care. In terms of complaints the outcome the CQC expect is for complainants and those acting on their behalf to have their comments and complaints listened to and acted on effectively, and to know that they will not be discriminated against for making a complaint.

Level Two: Health Service Ombudsman

The Parliamentary and Health Service Ombudsman (PHSO) is currently Ann Abraham, who took up her post in November 2002. She is independent of the NHS and of Government and derives her powers from the Health Service Commissioners Act 1993. The Ombudsman's Annual Report 'Bringing wider benefit from individual complaints' was published in October 2008: it confirmed the establishment of the new two-tier system and the increase in resources required to make this a reality. The Ombudsman has recruited significant numbers of new staff and opened a new office in Manchester.

www.ombudsman.org.uk/about-us/media-centre/press-releases/2008/pr2008-04.

Figure 23: The Parliamentary and Health Service Ombudsman's website (www.ombudsman.org.uk/).

Complaints that are not resolved locally by the practice may be referred directly to the Ombudsman. She can consider complaints on aspects of healthcare such as unsatisfactory care or treatment, including the exercise of clinical judgement, failure to provide a service that ought to be provided and poor administration.

The complainant can involve the Ombudsman at a number of stages in the process. In fact, the Ombudsman has the power to consider complaints that have not been put to the dentist, as well as cases where, although the first stage of the complaints procedure has not been exhausted, she considers that it is not reasonable to expect a successful outcome given the particular circumstances involved. Upon investigation the Ombudsman may uphold the complaint in full or in part, or may not uphold the complaint at all.

Where the complaint is at least partially upheld she may make recommendations for appropriate address, which might include:

- an apology
- an explanation
- improvements to practices or systems
- financial redress
- referral to the GDC.

The Ombudsman sometimes publishes particular cases (anonymised) where there are lessons to be learned and failings in services to patients. There is also extensive guidance on handling complaints.

Principles of Good Complaints handling. Parliamentary and Health Service Ombudsman, February 2009.

The General Dental Council and complaints

The GDC expects a practice to have in place a complaints procedure and to deal appropriately with any concerns or complaints raised by patients or their representatives, as part of dentists' professional relationship with patients. Their guidance underpins the first principle as stated in *Standards for dental professionals,* which is to 'put patients' interests first and act to protect them'. The guidance goes on to provide a checklist for complaint handling procedures including their final advice: 'above all, say and show how sorry you are that something has gone wrong'.

www.gdc-uk.org/News+publications+ and+events/Publications/Guidance+for+ dental+professionals/Standards+for+ dental+professionals.htm

Dental Complaints Service

This service for non-NHS complaints came into operation in May 2006 and is an independent service funded by the GDC through annual retention fees paid by registrants.

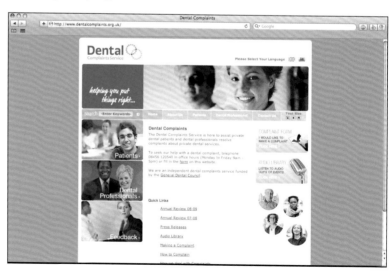

Figure 24: Dental Complaints Service website (http:/www.dentalcomplaints.org.uk).

The GDC, consumer organisations and the dental profession have long recognised the need for a scheme which deals with complaints about non-NHS dental care, since there was no equivalent to the NHS complaints scheme in private dentistry. The options open to patients in that situation were therefore very limited, and this service is intended to fill that void. The service has its own distinct identity, logo and brand, its own staff and administration, with an advisory board comprising GDC, patient/consumer and professional representation. It relates to the GDC but is separate from the GDC's formal regulatory procedures

Its processes are set out on its website, but essentially are intended to assist the patient in trying to resolve the complaint – first with the practice concerned, but, if unsuccessful, then to investigate the complaint itself via a panel hearing. On the Dental Complaints Service website there is a complaints form which patients can complete by filling in the boxes.

If the Dental Complaints Service staff fail to resolve the issue, the case goes before a panel drawn from over 150 lay and dental professional volunteers. Each panel is made up of two members of the public and one dental practitioner and both parties are invited to present their cases. No legal representation is allowed by either side and the service is free to both parties. The panel can make the following recommendations:

- The complaint is closed with no further action.
- No further action should be taken in relation to this specific complaint, but recommendations are made as to future practice.
- The dental professional should offer an apology to the patient.
- The dental professional should make recommendations as to future practice.
- The dental professional should make a full or partial refund of fees.
- The dental professional shall make a contribution towards the remedial treatment up to the cost of the original treatment.
- The dental professional shall endorse an agreement reached between the patient and the dental professional.

In exceptional circumstances, the panel may not be able to decide the outcome of a complaint. In these circumstances it may either record that a decision cannot be reached and/or ask for further information.

In the early days of the Dental Complaints Service there was some concern about its perceived lack of independence in dealing with complaints – perhaps unsurprisingly, given that it is funded by the GDC. This proved to be largely unfounded: both complainants and the profession rate the service quite highly. The majority of complaints logged by the Dental Complaints Service were resolved within three working days, according to the service's first annual report. The service logged more than 1,500 complaints in its first year of operation. More than half of the 1,559

Service helps resolve complaints in just three days. Dental Complaints Service (press release), December 2007.

complaints logged and closed by the Service in its first year were resolved over the phone, often by urging the patient and dental professional to talk.

Interestingly, one in six callers contacted the Service at the suggestion of a dental professional: this indicates the usefulness of the service as far as the profession is concerned. In terms of the demographic split the South East, London and the South West yielded most complaints per head of population; Scotland, the North East and – by far – Northern Ireland yielded least.

15 QUALITY AND CLINICAL GOVERNANCE

Performance management in the National Health Service reflects a desire for improvement, more efficiency, cost effectiveness and consistent quality. When the Labour Party came to power in 1997 these beliefs were the drivers behind the policy changes made to the NHS. As the then Health Secretary Frank Dobson wrote:

> For too long the emphasis has merely been on counting numbers, of measuring activity, of logging what could be logged, but this ignored the real needs of patients.
>
> Efficiency is also important. High quality and cost effectiveness are two sides of the same coin. Both are needed.

Frank Dobson. Foreword to *A First Class Service – Quality in the new NHS*. Department of Health, 1998.

The quality agenda was now part of the healthcare lexicon.

What is quality?

Quality itself is notoriously difficult to define. There are generic definitions in the form of famous sound-bites, such as Philip Crosby's view that quality is about 'zero defects' or Joseph Juran's perspective that it's about 'fitness for use'. (Both writers are well recognised in this field for their valuable contributions.) But, while such definitions are helpful in defining the big picture, they are of little value when analysing the individual elements of the quality agenda. For this purpose, disaggregated definitions are more appropriate where 'care' is typically defined by three components: the structure of care, the process of care and the outcomes of care. Such definitions acknowledge that quality is complex and it is possible to separate and study each individual component.

Philip Crosby, *Quality is Free* (1979).
Joseph Juran, *Juran's Quality Control Handbook* (1974).

Donabedian A. *An Introduction to Quality Assurance in Healthcare.* New York: Oxford University Press, 2003.

Clinical governance

Clinical governance (CG) has been an integral part of NHS dentistry for a decade. A duty of quality was placed on NHS organisations in the 1999 NHS Act. In Section 18(1) it states that:

> It is the duty of each Health Authority, Primary Care Trust and NHS Trust to put and keep in place arrangements for the purpose of moni-

toring and improving the quality of health care which it provides to individuals.

This Act introduced corporate accountability for clinical quality and performance.

The most frequently quoted definition describes clinical governance as

> a system through which NHS organisations are accountable for continuously improving the quality of their services and safeguarding high standards of care by creating an environment in which excellence in clinical care will flourish.

This definition, put forward by Scally and Donaldson in the *British Medical Journal*, emphasised the importance of continuous quality improvement and reduce variance in quality in healthcare organisations (see Figure 25).

Scally *et al.* (1998).

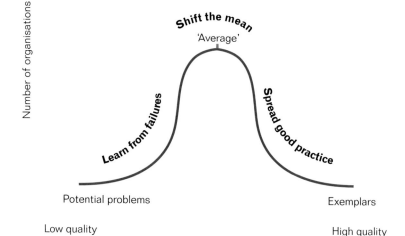

Figure 25 : The quality distribution curve.

As Figure 26 shows, Scally and Donaldson framed their model under six categories:

- infrastructure
- culture
- quality methods
- poor performance
- risk avoidance
- coherence.

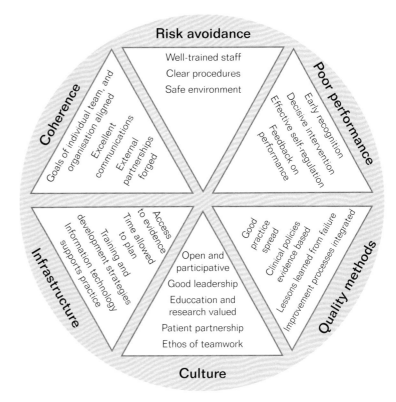

Figure 26: The integration of clinical governance.

Published in the *BMJ*,
16 August 2007; **335**
(doi: 10.1136/bmj.39308.477870.BD).

In England and Wales, clinical governance is the vehicle for the delivery of quality healthcare in the NHS. The Labour Government introduced the concept in 1999 in the white paper *The New NHS: Modern, Dependable*. It came about as a result of various high-profile media exposures of quality failure throughout the 1990s, which Tony Delamothe, Deputy Editor of the *BMJ*, described as the 'unholy trinity'. He was referring to the Shipman, Bristol, and Alder Hey enquiries which Roger Jones had described in an earlier correspondence as 'a litany of errors [that] shook the foundations of public trust and professional confidence.'

It was this issue about public trust and professional confidence that fuelled the Governance agenda which aimed to guarantee and deliver patient safety at its heart. The **National Patient Safety Agency** was established as an arm's length body of the Department of Health to promote patient safety in healthcare. It has three divisions:

1) National Reporting and Learning Service, which aims to reduce risks to patients receiving NHS care and improve safety.

2) National Clinical Assessment Service, which supports the resolution of concerns about the performance of individual clinical practitioners to help ensure their practice is safe and valued.

3) National Research Ethics Service, which protects the rights, safety, dignity and well-being of research participants that are part of clinical trials and other research within the NHS.

(Following the review of arm's length bodies in July 2010, the recommendation is that the National Clinical Assessment Service is to continue into the future.)

It was the Blair Government's first term, in 2001, that saw the beginnings of what is now the **National Institute for Health and Clinical Excellence** (NICE), which continues to support the Government's vision for an NHS focused on delivering the best possible outcomes for patients. NICE is a Special Health Authority for England and Wales. Its role is to provide patients and health professionals with 'authoritative, robust and reliable' guidance on current 'best practice'. NICE guidance covers three areas:

- **Clinical guidelines** – these cover the appropriate treatment and care of patients with specific diseases and conditions within the NHS in England and Wales.
- **Technology appraisals** – these cover the use of new treatments within the NHS in England and Wales.
- **Interventional procedures** – these cover the safety and efficacy of interventional procedures for diagnosis and treatment.

The publications relevant to dentistry are: Wisdom teeth – removal (2000); Dental recall (2004); Tooth decay – HealOzone (2005), Prophylaxis against infective endocarditis (March 2008). See www.nice.org.uk.

The guidance on Dental Recalls is one example of its impact on dentistry; in the current contract Clause 71 requires Providers to comply with published NICE guidance.

Contractual Requirements

In 2001, it became a requirement for dentists practising in the GDS to have a quality assurance system in place. The GDS Contract at the time introduced the concept of quality assurance into the GDS, under amendment 87 of the Terms of Service. The Health and Social Care (Community Health and Standards) Act 2003 refers to the 'duty of quality' and states that it is the duty of each NHS body to put and keep in place arrangements for the purpose of monitoring and improving the quality of healthcare provided by and for that body.

It is in Part 16 of the current GDS Contract that the present requirements are set out under the headings of clinical governance arrangements and quality assurance systems (see Table 15). Clause 245 permits changes to the governance agenda by stating explicitly the requirement to 'comply' with whatever arrangements may be in place. (The original wording on the contract read 'co-operate' but was changed shortly after publication to 'comply'; contractors were notified by an amendment notice in May 2006).

Clinical governance and the 2006 GDS Contract	
Clinical governance arrangements	
245.	The Contractor shall comply with such clinical governance arrangements as the PCT may establish in respect of Contractors providing services under a GDS Contract.
246.	The Contractor shall nominate a person who –
246.1.	will have responsibility for ensuring co-operation with clinical governance arrangements; and
246.2.	performs or manages services under the Contract.
Quality assurance system	
247.	The Contractor shall establish, and operate in accordance with clauses 248 and 249, a practice-based quality assurance system which is applicable to all the persons specified in clause 248.
248.	The specified persons are:
248.1.	any dental practitioner who performs services under the Contract;
248.2.	any other person employed or engaged by the Contractor to perform or assist in the performance of services under the Contract.
249.	The Contractor shall ensure that in respect of his practice-based quality assurance system, he has nominated a person (who need not be connected with the Contractor's practice) to be responsible for operating that system.
250.	In clauses 247 to 249, 'practice-based quality assurance system' means one which comprises a system to ensure that
250.1.	effective measures of infection control are used,
250.2.	all legal requirements relating to health and safety in the workplace are satisfied,
250.3.	all legal requirements relating to radiological protection are satisfied, and
250.4.	any requirements of the General Dental Council in respect of the continuing professional development of dental practitioners are satisfied,
250.5.	the requirement to display in a prominent position the written statement relating to the quality assurance system (see clause 208) is satisfied.

Table 15: Clinical governance and the 2006 GDS Contract.

Between 2006 and through to early 2010, the framework that many PCTs used for quality was a framework developed by the Healthcare Commission.

The Healthcare Commission

The Healthcare Commission was the name of the independent inspectorate body for the NHS in England; the legal name is the 'Commission for Healthcare Audit and Inspection'. It was formed by the Health and Social Care (Community Health and Standards) Act 2003, and launched on 1 April 2004. It replaced and took over the functions of a number of regu-

www.healthcarecommission.org.uk.

lators of the NHS, including its predecessor the Commission for Health Improvement (CHI) with a statutory duty to

- assess the management, provision and quality of NHS healthcare and public health services
- review the performance of each NHS trust
- regulate the independent healthcare sector through registration, annual inspection, monitoring complaints and enforcement
- publish information about the state of healthcare
- consider complaints about NHS organisations that the organisations themselves have not resolved
- promote the co-ordination of reviews and assessments carried out by ourselves and others
- carry out investigations of serious failures in the provision of healthcare.

It achieved this by developing a quality framework which consisted of 24 core and 13 developmental standards which set out the level of quality all organisations providing NHS care should meet or aspire to.

Standards for Better Health

This framework was driven by the publication *Standards for Better Health*, which set out the level of quality that all organisations providing NHS care will be expected to meet or aspire to across the NHS in England.

The focus was on providing a common set of requirements, using the core and development standards, and applying them across all healthcare organisations to ensure that health services are provided that are both safe and of an acceptable quality.

The 24 core standards described the level of quality that healthcare organisations, including dental practices, were expected to meet. They set out the minimum level of service that patients have a right to expect. The Healthcare Commission was resolute about the framework, stating that 'meeting the core standards is not optional'. In addition to the core standards, there are a number of developmental standards which reflect the increasing drive towards continuous quality improvement in the NHS. The core standards are prefixed with the letter C and the developmental standards are prefixed with the letter D. The standards are grouped into a framework comprising seven domains which are:

⬧ Annex B, 'Clinical governance framework', pp 205–7.

- ● **Safety**

  How do we manage and minimise risk in the practice? What systems and processes do we have in place to ensure patient safety?

- **Clinical and cost effectiveness**

  How are we ensuring that patients receive care and treatment that meet their individual needs? Do we apply research evidence to provide effective clinical outcomes?

- **Governance**

  How are we dealing with managerial responsibility, clinical leadership and professional accountability? What is the culture within the practice? What systems and working practices do we have in place to ensure that probity, quality assurance, quality improvement and patient safety are amongst the pillars of our practising philosophy?

- **Patient focus**

  How can we show that the services we provide are patient-centred? Are we respecting their diverse needs, preferences and choices? Are we working collaboratively with other organisations, like the secondary care sector or the community dental services, to ensure the patient journey is seamless?

- **Accessible and responsive care**

  Are patients receiving services as promptly as possible? Do they have a choice in access to services and treatments they receive? Do they experience unnecessary delays at any stage of service delivery?

- **Care environment and amenities**

  What is the physical environment like where patients are treated? Is it conducive to the well-being of patients and staff? Does it show respect for patients' needs and preferences? Is there adequate privacy? Are treatment rooms and waiting rooms well maintained, hygienic and clean?

- **Public health**

  How can we show that programmes and services are designed and delivered in collaboration with all relevant organisations and communities? How do we promote, protect and improve the health of the population at large to reduce health inequalities between different population groups and areas?

- **Domains and related standards**

  Within each domain there is an outcome statement and the intention is that by meeting the core standards, healthcare organisations and contractors will then achieve the desired outcome. This structure does address many of the early concerns expressed about clinical governance in the late 1990s – that the rhetoric focused on *what* rather than *how*.

This framework was used by PCTs in the context of dentistry and many Providers established systems and processes in their practices to meet the required standards.

The Healthcare Commission, together with the Commission for Social Care Inspection and the Mental Health Act Commission ceased to exist on 31 March 2009. In its place, is The Care Quality Commission – the new health and social care regulator for England.

The Care Quality Commission

The Care Quality Commission (CQC) is the independent regulator of health and social care in England. It aims to improve the standard of care to patients through four channels (Figure 27):

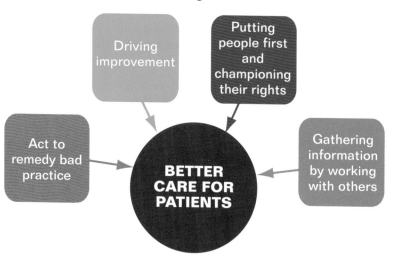

Figure 27: The drive for improvement.

The introduction to law of the Health and Social Care Act means primary dental care comes under the scope of the CQC's registration system from April 2011. As from 9 September 2010, dentists with NHS contracts will be contacted by the Care Quality Commission and invited to enrol for the application process online.

Registration is not just about the initial application and registration. The CQC will introduce a system of continuous monitoring and will hold a quality and risk profile, containing information relevant to registration, enabling them to assess where risks lie and support judgements on the quality of services (Figure 28).

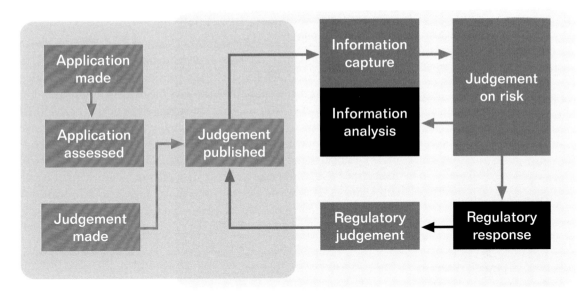

Figure 28: The CQC Registration Process.

The judgement on risk will undoubtedly underpin how the CQC attempts to address any shortcomings. This risk based assessment tool (Table 16) is to be welcomed as it will ensure that the level of concern will dictate the level of enforcement. The CQC have significant powers of enforcement, ranging from requesting action plans to imposing fines or ultimately closing down a service.

Table 16: Risk Assessment Matrix (CQC).

Likelihood	Low	Medium	high
Unlikely	Minor concern	Minor concern	Moderate concern
Possible	Minor concern	Moderate concern	Major concern
Almost certain	Moderate concern	Major concern	Major concern

The key questions that must be asked when concerns have been identified are :

- Has it happened before?
- How many people are exposed to the concern?
- Has the Provider identified the concern?
- Are measures in place to control the concern?
- Are all the relevant people in place managing the concern?

Essential standards of quality and safety

The CQC's guidance *Essential standards of quality and safety* describes what providers should do to meet these essential standards. In the last decade, quality improvement and assurance has been driven by an examination of structures and processes. In the early days the practice visit programme implemented by PCTs consisted almost exclusively of ticking boxes. These early initiatives then developed into a system- and process-driven format and the latest guidance pays homage to Donabedian's model by focusing on outcomes and the patient experience. As with *Standards for better health*, the CQC's guidance is generic; it applies to all providers of health and adult social care. At the time of writing, there is much discussion about how the outcomes should be interpreted for dentistry and what dentists need to do as the profession develops a strategy for implementation using existing CQC publications as a guide (Figure 29).

Figure 29: Three publications by the Care Quality Commission.

The essential standards of quality and safety consist of 28 regulations that are set out in two pieces of legislation:

- the Health and Social Care Act 2008 (Regulated Activities) Regulations 2010
- the Care Quality Commission (Registration) Regulations 2009.

For each regulation, there is an associated outcome – a patient-focused experience of care. As there are 28 regulations, so there are 28 outcomes. Compliance with the essential standards focuses on the 16 regulations (out of the 28) that come within Part 4 of the Health and Social Care Act 2008 (Regulated Activities) Regulations 2010 – these are the ones that most directly relate to the quality and safety of care, and Providers must have evidence that they meet the outcomes. These 16 regulations are summarised in Table 17.

Regulation*	Outcome	Title and summary of outcome
9	4	**Care and welfare of people who use services** People experience effective, safe and appropriate care, treatment and support that meets their needs and protects their rights.
10	16	**Assessing and monitoring the quality of service provision** People benefit from safe, quality care because effective decisions are made and because of the management of risks to people's health, welfare and safety.
11	7	**Safeguarding people who use services from abuse** People are safeguarded from abuse, or the risk of abuse, and their human rights are respected and upheld.
12	8	**Cleanliness and infection control** People experience care in a clean environment, and are protected from acquiring infections.
13	9	**Management of medicines** People have their medicines when they need them, and in a safe way. People are given information about their medicines.
14	5	**Meeting nutritional needs** People are encouraged and supported to have sufficient food and drink that is nutritional and balanced, and a choice of food and drink to meet their different needs.
15	10	**Safety and suitability of premises** People receive care in, work in or visit safe surroundings that promote their wellbeing.
16	11	**Safety, availability and suitability of equipment** Where equipment is used, it is safe, available, comfortable and suitable for people's needs.
17	1	**Respecting and involving people who use services** People understand the care and treatment choices available to them. They can express their views and are involved in making decisions about their care. They have their privacy, dignity and independence respected, and have their views and experiences taken into account in the way in which the service is delivered.

Regulation*	Outcome	Title and summary of outcome
18	2	**Consent to care and treatment** People give consent to their care and treatment, and understand and know how to change decisions about things that have been agreed previously.
19	17	**Complaints** People and those acting on their behalf have their comments and complaints listened to and acted on effectively, and know that they will not be discriminated against for making a complaint.
20	21	**Records** People's personal records are accurate, fit for purpose, held securely and remain confidential. The same applies to other records that are needed to protect their safety and wellbeing.
21	12	**Requirements relating to workers** People are kept safe, and their health and welfare needs are met, by staff who are fit for the job and have the right qualifications, skills and experience.
22	13	**Staffing** People are kept safe, and their health and welfare needs are met, because there are sufficient numbers of the right staff.
23	14	**Supporting workers** People are kept safe, and their health and welfare needs are met, because staff are competent to carry out their work and are properly trained, supervised and appraised.
24	6	**Co-operating with other providers** People receive safe and coordinated care when they move between providers or receive care from more than one provider.

Table 17: Essential standards of quality and safety – the 28 regulations (and associated outcomes).

It should be noted that the outcome numbers are different to the regulation numbers; this is because of the way the outcomes have been grouped in six categories or themes. The categories are:

- involvement and information
- personalised care, treatment and support
- safeguarding and safety
- suitability of staffing
- quality and management
- suitability of management.

The expectation is that 16 out of the 28 outcomes will be relevant to dentistry, though it must be noted that others may be relevant depending on how the CQC evolves the process for dentistry. The key 16 outcomes are summarised below:

Sixteen of these outcomes relate most directly to the quality of safety and care and will be the focus of CQC checks for compliance:

- **Involvement and information**
  Outcome 1: Respecting and involving people who use services
  Outcome 2: Consent to care and treatment
  Outcome 3: Personalised care, treatment and support
  Outcome 4: Care and welfare of people who use services
  Outcome 5: Meeting nutritional needs
  Outcome 6: Co-operating with other providers

- **Safeguarding and safety**
  Outcome 7: Safeguarding people who use services from abuse
  Outcome 8: Cleanliness and infection control
  Outcome 9: Management of medicines
  Outcome 10: Safety and suitability of premises
  Outcome 11: Safety, availability and suitability of equipment

- **Suitability of staffing**
  Outcome 12: Requirements relating to workers
  Outcome 13: Staffing
  Outcome 14: Supporting workers

- **Quality and management**
  Outcome 16: Assessing and monitoring the quality of service provision
  Outcome 17: Complaints
  Outcome 21: Records

The legislative framework that underpins this system gives the CQC extended powers. When non-compliance is reported and the practice has not completed action plans to improve performance, the CQC can take proportionate enforcement action: the risk assessment tool will be used to ensure that the response remains proportionate. The response could include warning notices, imposition or variation of conditions, suspension of registration to provide certain services, fines and prosecution – and, in extreme instances, cancellation of registration.

Information and performance management

Performance management of the contract is carried out at local level by PCTs. Key to delivering performance management is the collection of appropriate and timely information. The PCT has access to a number of sources of data required to carry out its performance management tasks.

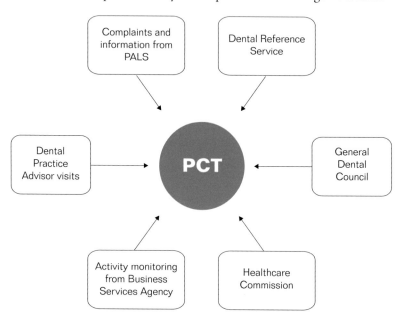

Figure 30: The PCT's sources of data.

Dental Reference Service

For the first three years of the 2006 contract the focus of the Dental Reference Service (DRS) was on clinical governance support and advice to general dental practices. The intention was to have a rolling programme of inspections: these would be carried out randomly but could also take place in response to any concerns PCTs had about a practice's performance or health and safety issues.

Outcomes of the Dental Reference Service Review *CDO Update* June 2008.

During 2007 the NHS Business Services Authority Dental Services Division (DSD) carried out a fundamental review of the DRS. In order to make best use of their dental reference officers, the DRS has returned to its familiar monitoring role. The DSD has adopted a risk-based approach to its services. It recognises that under the 2006 contract opportunities for inappropriate financial gain for Contractors and Performers are limited. Contract values are agreed in advance so that there will always be a ceiling on the annual amount of money a Provider can earn on the NHS. There are, however, opportunities to maximise the units of dental activity provided to reduce a Contractor's obligations under the contract.

The risk management role of the NHSBSA in NHS primary care dentistry; beyond payment and processing. *Dental Profile* 2006 www.nhsbsa.nhs.uk/DentalServices/1146.aspx.

Clinical Policy Advisors (CPAs) work with PCTs in the ten Strategic Health Authorities in England in developing effective risk-based processes. They act as the first point of contact for PCTs about clinical issues and are the hub for the co-ordination of risk-based information generated by DSD activities.

BSA Dental Service Division. CDO Update, December 2008, p14.

The aims of the DRS are to monitor remotely, where possible, in order to reduce the disruption to practices caused by DRS visits as well as to target DRS resources more effectively on quality outcomes. The DRS activity will integrate with other DSD monitoring information to provide a more complete picture of clinical quality in relation to particular contracts.

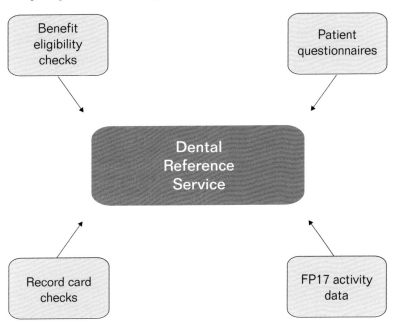

Figure 31: DRS monitoring information.

Benefit eligibility checks

Certain categories of patients are exempt from NHS treatment charges. These include:

- a person under 18 years of age
- a person aged 18 and in full-time education
- an expectant mother
- a woman who has had a baby or a still-birth in the previous 12 months
- a person on Income Support
- a person on Jobseeker's Allowance (income-based)
- a person with Working Tax Credit/Child Tax Credit and meeting certain conditions
- a person with Pension Credit Guarantee Credit either paid on its own or with Savings Credit.

These categories may vary from time to time.

Dental points of treatment checks – a guide for dentists, orthodontists and dental staff. NHS Counter Fraud and Security Management Services, September 2006.

Contractors are required to check a patient's eligibility for dental treatment and declare on the FP17 whether or not they have seen any evidence of exemption. Dentists dealing with claim forms will not be held responsible if patients do not provide evidence or provide evidence that is false. The DSD selects a daily sample of FP17s where the patient has claimed help with NHS dental charges and carries out verification checks to establish whether the patient was entitled to that help.

Each month they send details of the selected claims to the Department of Work & Pensions and they check their records to confirm whether the patient was entitled to help with NHS dental charges. Over a million claims per year are selected for checking. To follow up cases where eligibility was not not confirmed, a questionnaire is sent to the patient asking them to confirm that the DSD have the correct details and asking if the patient qualified for help with NHS charges for any reason other than that shown on the information the dentist sent to the DSD. The questionnaire also asks the patient to send evidence that they were entitled to help with NHS dental charges.

If the DSD still cannot confirm that the patient was entitled to help, it has to verify that the patient's declaration was signed and completed properly. This is an essential part of the process, as the patient's declaration is the evidence that the patient made a claim for help with NHS dental charges. It is important therefore that Contractors ensure that where forms are transmitted electronically the patient's declaration (PR) form is signed and retained.

Where the DSD cannot confirm that a patient was entitled to the help claimed it is required to recover the charge that should have been paid. They are also required to issue a penalty notice, where appropriate. If the debt is not paid, they will start debt recovery proceedings through the County Court.

Questionnaires

Twenty-five thousand questionnaires are sent out every month and by the end of 2007/2008 every health body had in excess of 1,000 FP17s selected for patient questionnaires.

The questionnaire seeks to establish that:

- the patient exists
- the patient attended the dentist on the dates reported
- treatment appropriate to the band claimed was provided
- the patient paid an appropriate charge and understands the charge bands
- there were overall levels of satisfaction with the NHS treatment received.

▶ p 144.

A report is sent to the PCT and part of the information is extracted to be used in the Vital Signs report which is used for contract monitoring purposes.

Record card checks

The DSD carries out random administrative checks on records and there is a rolling programme where each PCT area will have request for Contractors to send ten record cards per contract. These are not checked by clinicians but the following information is checked:

- how well the information from the FP17 matches the record card
- private treatment: could it have been provided under NHS arrangements?
- is the patient exempt but the card shows patient charge but no evidence of private treatment?
- FP17 PR – is it present?
- FP17DC – is it present if required?
- lab work documents – are they available?
- medical history – is there one present and signed by the patient?
- charting-baseline
- radiographs – is there a record of their justification and a report present and are they properly labelled?
- photographs
- charge exempt items.

FP17 activity data

A significant amount of information is collected from FP17s and this can be reported on in a number of different ways. There are standard reports including the Vital Signs reports, but the DSD can provide more detailed reports on a patient-by-patient basis if required by the PCT.

DRS practice visits

The Dental Reference Service can carry out practice visits. There are three components to a DRS visit to a practice and a PCT may elect to ask for a combination of them: environment check; clinical inspection of two to four patients; record card audit.

A reasonable period of notice is usually given for a visit to ensure minimum disruption to your practice. A practice with three dentists would take between one to two days to inspect if all three areas are reviewed. The NHS is committed to raising the quality of care for patients, while at the same time ensuring that treatment is provided as cost effectively as possible. The PCT needs to ensure that not only are the contractually agreed units of dental activity delivered by the practice, but also the environment in which they are delivered is modern, safe and fit for purpose.

A way of looking at the different performance indicators in a Mid-year or Annual Review is to look at:

- quantitative measures
- qualitative measures
- processes and protocols
- staff and resources.

▶ p 208.
See the 'Performance monitoring matrix' in Annex C to this chapter.

Environment check

This is an in-depth practice inspection covering health and safety. The proforma used is a 19-page document covering the following areas:

SV9 Practice Inspection proforma (www.nhsbsa.nhs.uk/DentalServices/848.aspx).

- health and safety
- ionising radiation regulations
- complaint handling
- written policies in a number of areas such as infection control and employment policies
- staff training details
- toilet facilities.

It is exceptionally detailed and requires considerable preparatory time to ensure the appropriate protocols and documentation are available.

The DRS has developed a self assessment tool (SAT) which can be completed by Contractors via the PCT. A proportion of the completed SATs can be randomly selected for surgery inspection by the DRS to validate responses.

Clinical inspection of four patients

Four patients will be chosen by the Dental Reference Service, based on submissions made on FP17 in relation to completed treatment and in order to provide assurance in relation to specific quality issues. The Dental Reference Officer will examine the patient and then discuss issues such as patient management, treatment planning and other clinical issues. As these will be targeted at specific concerns all the patients examined may have had certain types of treatment provided, e.g. crown, root canal therapy. The clinical issues discussed will relate to those areas.

Record card audit

As part of the quality assurance process some records will be randomly selected by the DRO – perhaps the first five from the previous day's daylist – and these will be assessed according to certain criteria. There are key pieces of information required in records and a useful guide has been issued by the Faculty of General Dental Practitioners.

Clinical Examination and Record Keeping – Good practice guidelines. FGDP, 2001.

A written record should contain:

- up-to date medical history
- the date, diagnosis and treatment notes every time the patient is seen, with full details of any particular incidents, episodes or discussions including options
- monitoring information such as Basic Periodontal Examination (BPE) scores, periodontal probing depths and other indices, tracking oral pathology and other conditions
- all payments made by the patient.
- all correspondence to and from the patient, or any third party (consultant, other dentists, doctor, etc.)
- consents obtained and warnings and information given
- findings/diagnosis on radiographs – particularly if discovered after the patient has left the surgery
- drugs and dosages given.

Based on Rattan *et al.* (2004), p 95.

There are ten essential requirements in clinical record keeping.

● **Identification data**
These will include name, address, telephone numbers and e-mail addresses. Text messages (SMS: short message service) are being increasingly used by practices to remind patients of appointments and so mobile phone numbers are useful.

● **Medical history**
This should be in the form of a written proforma which will cover all aspects of the patient's general health. This should be signed and dated by the patient and have a space for the treating dentist to date every time the medical history is checked at recalls. There should be an enquiry about smoking and alcohol consumption.

● **Dental history**
This should cover previous dental experiences, why the patient has come to the particular practice as well as an understanding of risk factors such as diet and oral hygiene measures. Lifestyle questions about attitudes to dentistry and cosmetic treatment can be covered in a questionnaire.

● **Clinical examination**
This clinical examination should cover both extra-oral as well as intra-oral structures including an oral cancer screening. Both negative and positive findings should be recorded. A baseline charting to include the current status of the teeth and supporting periodontal structures should be undertaken with a record that this has been done. A BPE or some other equivalent objective measurement should be recorded.

● **Radiographic examination**

Any radiographs taken should be justified and the report on any findings should be in the notes.

● **Diagnosis**

Very few notes record a diagnosis except for the most common pericorinitis. A diagnosis gives a rationale for treatment and should be present even for routine fillings, e.g. 'recurrent caries – broken filling' or 'irreversible pulpitis'.

● **Treatment plan**

A list of treatment to be done as well as any referral that needs to be made should be recorded. This allows the proper sequencing of treatment according to appropriate principles of relief of pain first, followed by increasingly complex treatment depending on the patient's response to prevention and other advice.

● **Reference to consent**

The options available should be discussed and recorded as well as the relevant advantages and disadvantages. The patient's preference for a particular treatment should be recorded and the reasons for doing so, especially if the dentist is not in complete agreement. There is a requirement in the new Regulations that the patient should have a choice of dentist and this should be recorded.

● **Progress notes**

These will form the bulk of the records and should always be dated and a note made of the treating dentist. The nurse's initials are also useful. The treatments undertaken, details of local anaesthetics and any instructions given should be noted. Some warnings may be given as standard and therefore, to avoid continually recording them, an advice sheet can be given and a copy retained in the file for future reference. These may be on post-extraction instruction, advice about orthodontic appliances or the care of dentures.

● **Exit notes**

If a patient informs the practice that they are leaving it is useful to record the reasons for the departure. This is particularly so if they are in the middle of treatment. Many practices send questionnaires to patients who have not visited the practice for some time and these will assist in developing a customer-friendly approach to patient care. Some patients may request copies of their notes or radiographs when they leave: they are entitled to these under the Data Protection Act.

The DSD has a grid (SV11) to enable an audit to be carried out by the Dental Reference Officer in the practice. The following categories will be checked and ticked for each record card audited if the criteria are satisfied.

Patient Records

1) **Patient Identifiers.** A clinical record needs to include basic information which specifically identifies the patient i.e. name, date of birth, address, etc. Failure to do so results in poor administration, lost records etc.

2) **Medical history.** Each patient should have a medical history recorded which should be signed by the patient. It should be updated at the start of each new course of treatment and when interventions are carried out. Failure to do this would mean that a patient who has a serious medical condition or who is on certain medications does not have this identified. The potential result can be fatal or cause serious detriment to a patient's health. The DRO will want to ensure that there are robust systems to ensure that all medical histories are recorded and updated and will suggest improvements to practice processes to assist the dentist in this.

3) **Charting.** This falls into three sections:
   a) **Charting of the teeth** – This maintains a pictorial record of the mouth including fillings, crowns, extractions etc and assists in treatment planning and identification of the patient.
   b) **Charting of the gum (periodontal) condition** usually using the BPE (Basic Periodontal Examination). This ensures that gum disease does not go undetected and helps to record the progress of any gum disease and the success of treatment and improvements in the patient's oral care.
   c) **Soft tissue examination.** This must be done and recorded at the start of every course of treatment to ensure the early detection of soft tissue disease, in particular cancer of the mouth.

4) **Patient information.** This is to ensure the record includes a note of any explanation/discussion with the patient as part of informed consent.

5 **Treatment Planning/Treatment provision.** The clinical records should include a note of treatment planned and treatment provided. This gives a narrative of the progress of treatment. It should be comprehensive enough to include details of individual teeth, materials, local anaesthetics, complications etc. Failure to do this could result in poor treatment planning; any subsequent query or complaint would not be dealt with satisfactorily.

6) **Recall Interval.** New contractual arrangements require dentists to carry out a risk assessment for each patient using the NICE guidelines on recall intervals, and decide, after discussion with the patient, the recall interval appropriate. They need to take into account the patient's risk factors for dental disease, e.g. sugar consumption, oral hygiene, tobacco and alcohol consumption (both of which increase the risk of oral cancer). The DRO will help to ensure that low risk patients are not seen frequently, reducing access, and high risk patients are appropriately monitored.

7) **Administration.** The DRO reviews administration to ensure records are kept securely and confidentially.

8) **Radiographs.** Under the Ionising Regulations IR (ME) R 2000 regulations, practitioners are required to justify why radiographs are to be taken, ensure they are using an appropriate view and write an

evaluation of each film. They should also have a quality assurance system in place. The DRO checks each of these aspects and advises the dentist accordingly. Although dental X-rays are generally of low dosage, failure to conform to IR(ME)R 2000 can potentially result in unnecessary exposure of patients to ionising radiation with the attendant increased risk of malignancy, etc.

- **Justification.** The dentist should carry out a risk assessment for each film to ensure that the benefit to the patient of the information a film will provide outweighs the exposure to radiation necessary, i.e. that the film is justified.
- **Appropriate view.** This also includes the careful choice of appropriate view to ensure the lowest dose of radiation is used to provide most benefit.
- **Frequency.** The DRO will review the dentist's process for this to help ensure that radiographs are used optimally and at the appropriate frequency depending on the patient's risk status.
- **Clinical Evaluation.** All films must be reviewed by the dentist after they have been taken and the results of what was found written in the patient's notes. This is to help ensure that no pathology on the film is missed and if the film is lost a repeat will not be necessary.
- **Film Quality.** The DRO will check that a quality assurance programme is in place. Films of poor quality may not be diagnostic and the dentist may then have to repeat them, doubling the radiation exposure to the patient. A quality assurance programme identifies less satisfactory films and the causes can be identified and remedied.
- **Administration.** The DRO reviews, for example, the mounting, storage, labelling of films to ensure accurate retrieval. Sequential films can then be used easily to review conditions which are being monitored. In addition the operator should be identified so that the QA system reveals any individual performance problems.

Patient Care

1) **Effective provision of preventative dentistry.** The DRO completes a questionnaire with each patient examined which explores their risk factors for dental disease, i.e. sugar consumption, oral and denture hygiene, smoking, alcohol consumption, family history of dental disease. They then ask if the practitioner and their team have given preventive advice and consider the effectiveness of prevention. This also permits an informed discussion with the dentist about the recall interval suitable for that patient.

2) **Treatment options and treatment provided.** The questionnaire also includes an assessment of the patient's understanding of the treatment they have had and what their alternative options might have been. This helps ensure that the dentist and their team are communicating effectively.

3) **Patient attitude/satisfaction.** The patient's attitude and their satisfaction with the treatment and the dental team are assessed with feedback to the dentist when necessary.

ANNEX B
Clinical governance framework

Theme	Requirements – key actions and policies
1. Infection Control C1, C4, C10, C20, C21, D1, D12, D13	Procedures in accordance with BDA/DH Advice sheet A12 (Infection Control in Dentistry) including: • Infection control policy • Inoculation injury policy and recording of Hepatitis B immunisation status of exposure prone staff • Staff induction programme to include infection control procedures and staff training • Audit of policy compliance
2. Child Protection C2, C6, C10	• Identification and CRB checks for all staff • Child protection policy which is consistent with local and wider policies including any staff training requirements
3. Dental Radiography C1, C11, C24	Procedures and policies in accordance with the IRR(1999) and IR(ME)R (2000) including: • A quality assurance system • X-ray malfunction plan, including how to manage an unintended over-exposure; • Records of staff training and updates. • X-ray equipment maintenance records
4. Staff, Patient, Public and Environmental Safety C1, C4, C5, C20, C21, D12	• Significant events analysis procedures and changes to procedures initiated as a result • Compliance with Reporting of Injuries, Diseases and Dangerous Occurrences Regulations (RIDDOR) 1995 • Procedures to ensure all relevant safety alert bulletins are disseminated to staff and acted on • All medical devices are CE compliant, staff training for usage provided and incident reporting carried out • Medicines are appropriately sourced, purchased and stored including a medical emergencies drug kit • Compliance with Carriage of Dangerous Goods and Use of Transferable Pressure Equipment (Amendment) Regulations, 2005 • Hazardous waste regulations 2005 and the management of waste amalgam/mercury • Health and Safety at Work Act 1974 • Management of Health and Safety at work Regulations 1999 • Workplace (Health, Safety and Welfare) Regulations 1992 • Control of Substances Hazardous to Health Regulations 2002 (Also see *Infection Control*, *Child Protection* and *Dental Radiography*)

Theme	Requirements – key actions and policies
5. Evidenced-Based Practice and Research C1 C3 C5 C12 D2 D11	• Relevant NICE Guidelines are followed • Clinical care is informed by other evidence-based guidelines • Existing care pathways and referral protocols are followed • Where appropriate, principles of research governance are applied
6. Prevention and Public Health C22, C23, D13	An evidence-based prevention policy for all oral diseases and conditions appropriate to the needs of the local population and consistent with local and national priorities. This should include: • Links to any existing community based strategies • Tobacco use cessation • Alcohol consumption advice (Also see *Infection Control, Patient, Public and Environmental Safety*)
7. Clinical records, patient privacy and confidentiality C9, C13, C20	• Staff awareness of and compliance with Data Protection Act 1998 • Caldicott Guidelines 1997, Access to Health Records 1998 and Confidentiality Code of Practice 1998 are followed • Confidentiality policy • Satisfactory arrangements for confidential discussions with patients • Data protection policy
8. Staff Involvement and Development (for all staff) C5, C7, C8, C10 C11, C21, C24, D7, D12	• Employment policies – appropriate job descriptions for all posts • Appraisal, personal development plans and links to mentoring schemes • Appropriate staff training undertaken and records of staff training maintained (e.g. customer training, equal opportunities, dealing with complaints and patient feedback) • Records of practice meetings and evidence of staff involvement • Protected time for staff meetings and clinical governance • Confidential process for staff to raise concerns about performance • Links to a local Practitioner Advice and Support Scheme (PASS) or similar • Evidence of regular basic life support training • Evidence that staff opinion is sought about practice matters (e.g. staff surveys, practice meeting)
9. Clinical Staff Requirements and Development C4, C5, C10, C11	(Items listed under *Staff Involvement and Development* also apply) All GDC requirements are met including: • GDC registration/enrolment where appropriate • Supervision of clinical staff • Continuing Professional Development requirements • Handling of complaints • Dealing with poor performance (including 'whistle blowing' policy)

Theme	Requirements – key actions and policies
10. Patient Information and Involvement C3, C7, C13, C14, C16, C17, C18, C19, C21, D2, D3, D5, D8, D9, D10, D11	• Patients' and carers' views on services are sought and acted upon • Patients have opportunities to ask questions and provided with sufficient information to make informed decisions about their care • Patient information leaflets are available in languages appropriate to the local population • Well-publicised complaints system that is supportive of patients • Other patient feedback methods are available (e.g. suggestion boxes) • Evidence that practice has acted on findings of patient feedback • Information for patients on how to access NHS care in and out of hours
11. Fair and accessible care C7, C13, C18, C19, C21, D11	(Items listed under *Patient Information and Involvement* may also apply) • Compliance with the Race Relations (Amendment) Act 2000 and Human Rights Act 1998 • Access to interpreting services • All reasonable efforts made to comply with the Disability Discrimination Act 1995 • Emergency/urgent appointments available during the day
12. Clinical Audit and Peer Review C5, D1, D3, D4, D5	• All staff involved in identifying priorities for and involved in clinical audit or peer review • Evidence of compliance with any locally agreed requirements for clinical audit or peer review • Evidence that changes have been made where necessary, as a result of clinical audit or peer review

Practice development
　　Practice management
　　Staff training
　　Appraisal
　　Personal development plans

Activity　　UDAs

Additional services
　　Sedation
　　Domiciliary Care
　　Emergency out-of-hours care
　　Dental public health services

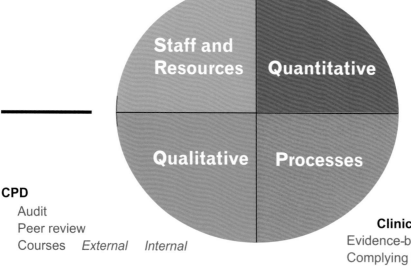

Staff and Resources | Quantitative
Qualitative | Processes

CPD
　Audit
　Peer review
　Courses　*External*　*Internal*

Clinical governance
　　Evidence-based protocols
　　Complying with NICE guidance
　　Significant event audit

Patient satisfaction
　　Patient information leaflet
　　Complaints monitoring
　　Patient choice
　　Survey

Quality assurance system

Charges
　　Patient information on charges/
　　receipts for NHS payments

Checks
　　on qualifications of DCPs
　　on performers compliance with eligibility
　　on clinical references for performers
　　on professional indemnity for performers

Practice inspection
　　Record checks
　　Environment checks
　　Access by PCT / Patient Forums

Part Four

FUTURE PLANNING

16 BUSINESS CONSIDERATIONS

A New Contract, new Regulations, the lifting of many restrictions for the provision of care and treatments that were in the Statement of Dental Remuneration, local contracting and, in time, local commissioning, new payment arrangements, new metrics for measuring performance and a host of related changes have introduced challenges and made demands of practice owners on a scale never encountered before.

The changes necessitate a radical rethink of the business model of running a general dental practice and require dentists to revisit their business strategy. A task of this magnitude requires knowledge, insight and discipline. One way to create the necessary focus is to use well-tested business management tools and frameworks. This chapter looks at some of those which dentists may find useful for managing their practice in the new National Health Service.

There are a number of business planning frameworks which can be used in practice development.

The Five Forces Model

Professor Michael Porter's model is a competition model and is well suited to general dental practice in the new NHS. Like it or not, practices within Primary Care Trusts are in competition for growth funding and need to understand the vectors that drive the purchasing decisions from PCTs.

Porter's model (Figure 32) provides a framework that allows us objectively to understand where we are in the marketplace in relation to others around us. The concept involves a relationship between competitors within an industry, suppliers, buyers and alternative solutions to the problem being addressed. The model shows five main factors that are key to influencing your practice performance.

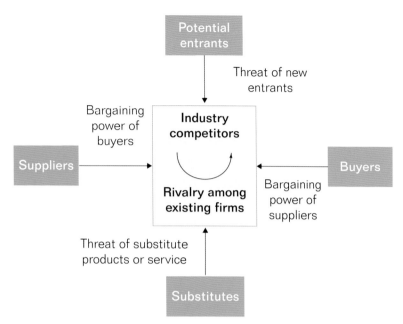

Figure 32: The Five Forces Model.

Competitive rivalry

This is a good starting point. Competitive rivalry will be high if:

- There is little differentiation between the products and services offered by different practices. This is likely to be the case in areas where NHS services are easily accessible and offered by all or most practices in your area.
- The competitors all have similar strategies.
- All or most practices in the area wish to grow and there are limited funds available. In this case all practices are competing for the same (limited) budget, thus increasing competitive rivalry.

In contrast, industry rivalry will be reduced if some or many practices in your area have chosen to move away from the NHS. These practices will no longer be your competitors for the primary dental care budget at the PCT. Their business strategy will also be different and therefore not directly competitive – although there may be similarities because it is likely that practices offering NHS services will also offer private services.

Power of suppliers

In the context of GDS Contract, the suppliers are the Providers. They are essential to the success of the service. The power of the Providers increases if they are amongst only a minority in a given area and there is no substitute for their services. This favours the practices which are sited in areas where provision of and access to NHS services are limited.

Power of buyers

The PCT is the buyer of the service. The power of the buyer increases when there is a surplus of Providers because tenders can be invited for the provision of services. This could lead to more competitive tendering from the suppliers (practices), thereby driving down the contract price. This is seen as a threat by many in areas where buyers have a strategic advantage.

Threat of substitutes

Ask yourself the question: how else could the PCT purchase NHS services and offer patients the same benefit for the same or a less price? The threat of substitute is high when a substitute Provider can offer the same service at a lesser price and the buyers (PCT) are willing and able to offer a substitute service.

Threat of new entrant

The threat of a new practice entering the area is high when entry barriers are low. Advertisements from PCTs are starting to appear in the dental press inviting tenders from interested parties who wish to establish new services in certain areas.

The Balanced Score card

Kaplan *et al.* (1992).

Selected by *Harvard Business Review* as one of the 'most important management practices of the past 75 years', the concept of the Balanced Score card has been translated into more than 19 languages. It was devised by Robert Kaplan and David Norton in the early 1990s and is a mechanism for developing and articulating your business strategy.

It will help you to answer two key questions:

- What does your practice need to do to succeed in the new NHS?
- How can we get all the Performers and team members working towards our goals?

The mix of financial and non-financial measures in the score card (Figure 33) can help you and your team focus on how to develop your practice in the new NHS. By applying the framework to your practice, you can develop a series of business objectives and targets and identify the measures you need to monitor your progress. The template worksheet (Table 18) may help you with this.

♦ p 214.

Mission and vision

Your mission is a concise, internally focused statement (the so-called mission statement) of the reason for the existence of your practice. In other words, it should reflect the core purpose of being and the values guiding the activities of your team. It is linked with your core values and should describe how you deliver value to your patients.

In contrast, your vision is a statement that describes your long-term goals. It is usually external and therefore market-oriented – it defines how your practice wants to be perceived by those outside.

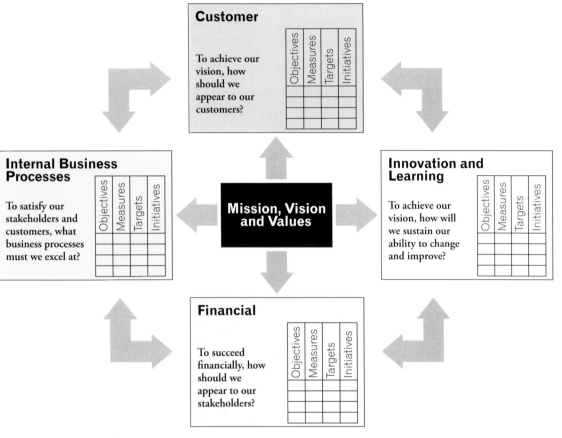

Customer

To achieve our vision, how should we appear to our customers?

Objectives | Measures | Targets | Initiatives

Internal Business Processes

To satisfy our stakeholders and customers, what business processes must we excel at?

Objectives | Measures | Targets | Initiatives

Mission, Vision and Values

Innovation and Learning

To achieve our vision, how will we sustain our ability to change and improve?

Objectives | Measures | Targets | Initiatives

Financial

To succeed financially, how should we appear to our stakeholders?

Objectives | Measures | Targets | Initiatives

Figure 33: The Balanced Score card.

With the introduction of the 2006 contract, many practices have felt it necessary to rethink their purpose and intent. As a result they have reviewed their mission and vision statements to reflect the new arrangements, For some, the changes have induced a radical re-think of their objectives, while others have elected to 'carry on as usual'.

The financial perspective

Financial data relating to contract values, cash flow, expense ratios and fixed and variable costs are traditional measures. Financial ratios such as return on investment (ROI) and cost benefit analyses are more sophisticated measures and practice owners should liaise with their professional advisers to see how their financial statistics compare with national benchmark figures.

The patient perspective

Patient focus and patient satisfaction are the drivers of business success in general dental practice. Dissatisfied patients will seek care and treatment elsewhere; their loss is a leading indicator of future decline. It takes time for the effect of this to permeate though the practice and damage to the business may not be evident for some time.

Name of Practice: _____

Balanced Score card Category	Main Objective(s)	Key Measure(s)	Target(s)	Overall Initiative(s)
Financial How do you perceive the financial performance of your practice? What is the strategy for growth, profitability, and risk viewed from the perspective of the PCT?				
Patients How do our patients perceive us? What is the strategy for creating value and differentiation from the perspective of the patient?				
Internal Business Processes At what processes must we excel? What are the strategic priorities for various business processes, which create satisfaction for the patient and the PCT?				
Learning and Innovation How do we sustain our ability to be innovative and to change with the 2006 contract? What are the priorities to create a climate that supports practice change, innovation and growth?				

Table 18: Balanced Score card Worksheet.

In developing metrics for satisfaction, patients should be grouped according to their needs and wants and how the practice is meeting these diverse needs. In looking at the patient perspective, you will need to consider your position with regard to the following:

- patient selection
- new patient acquisition
- patient retention
- patient growth.

These will need to be considered alongside the financial perspective given the fixed budgets and UDA targets assigned to practices. Simple measures such as patient surveys, how long it takes to answer telephone calls, number of complaints and other forms of patient feedback are all useful indicators.

The business process perspective

Metrics based on the business perspective allow Contractors to measure how well the practice is running, and whether its products and services satisfy patients' requirements – the 'mission' for any practice, irrespective of the market it chooses to serve.

Learning and innovation

This perspective includes team training and continuing professional development for all team members. 'Learning' is more than 'training'. It should include mentors and tutors and systems that allow team members to receive support and advice when they experience difficulties. The practice culture should be supportive of this. The purpose and intent is reflected in the principles of clinical governance.

Risk and opportunity in the new NHS

The frameworks under discussion should help you better plan the future strategy for your practice – whether or not you choose to continue to provide NHS services.

The outcome of the decision-making process will vary amongst practices, depending on the perception of risk. To say that we practise in uncertain times is an understatement: our future success will depend on how we cope and manage uncertainty. Uncertainty can be perceived as positive opportunity or negative threat.

Looking back, there can be little doubt that one of the attractions of PDS was the mitigation of business risk. The practices which were attracted to a like-for-like swap secured and underpinned the business model; some of those with growth prospects were able to secure additional funding to develop their practices. For this cohort, PDS came as a positive opportunity. For the remainder, there remain more questions than answers, even less consensus and still more uncertainty about what direction to take after April 2006. For them, the concerns reflect a negative threat.

By exercising internal controls, dentists can do one or more of the following.

- **Tolerate the risk** – It may be that you are not in a position to make any radical changes to your practice and that you decide to simply tolerate the risk, in which case it is a good idea to have a contingency plan in mind for your 'What if?' scenario.
- **Treat the risk** – This means make changes designed to constrain the risk to an acceptable level.
- **Transfer the risk** – This should always be part of risk management but is beyond the scope of this book.
- **Terminate the activity that gives rise to the risk in the first place** – If you believe that the risks associated with the new NHS are intolerable then consider withdrawing the facility from your practice.

Adopting this approach is to create a level of risk (known as residual risk), exposure to which is *acceptable to the individual or the business.* The risk appetite amongst dentists will vary from person to person and will be determined by age, ambition and business objectives; the perception of this risk therefore takes place within the context of the environment and personal circumstances. The balanced score card should assist you in mapping out your own position.

The process of weighing up the pros and cons of the various options is a risk *assessment.* This risk assessment should focus on two parameters – the likelihood of the risk being realised and the impact of the consequences. These are often expressed in a 3 by 3 matrix (Figure 34), although a 5 by 5 matrix is also popular. The significance of the risk is usually identified by a colour: in this case, the green and yellow zones fall on the tolerable side of the grid (shown by the thick black line) while the red zones represent unacceptable levels. Because the assessment is subjective – depending on an individual's risk appetite – and because all practices have a different business profile, dentists will differ in how they see the impact of the changes to NHS dentistry.

Positioning your practice on this grid for each of the risks associated with the changes is not an easy task and requires careful thought and analysis.

▶ p 218.
Managing the business of dentistry requires a careful assessment of all the risks associated with running a modern dental practice. The types of risk and the possible outcomes are summarised in Table 19.

By the process of systematically working through this table and plotting the outcome for each category on the matrix shown in Figure 34, you can build up a picture for your practice. Your picture will be different from that of your friends and colleagues and your decision about the future of your business should be based on this analysis.

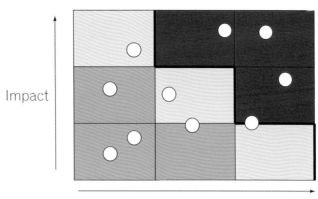

Figure 34: Probability-impact
matrix.

We must not forget that for a modern practice to deliver quality care to its patients both in terms of product and service quality, it has to be profitable and manage a range of commercial risks. The threat that an event or circumstance will adversely affect a practice's ability to achieve its strategic objectives and reduce the expected or anticipated profitability can have a negative impact on patient care. That is an unacceptable price to pay for anyone in a healthcare profession.

This may be a time for collective responsibility, but it is not a time for collective decision-making – that should be done in relation to your personal appetite for risk and reward.

Type of business risk	Possible outcomes
Capital risk	The risk that all or part of your capital, your original investment, will not be returned to you if the practice fails or is unable to secure the desired contract value.
Credit risk	The concern that the practice may not be able to meet its financial commitments in terms of repayments on loans. This has happened in some cases where practices have been established outside the test period and have not secured the level of funding they had anticipated in line with their growth projections under previous GDS arrangements and have now been forced to take drastic measures to protect themselves.
Inflation risk	The concern that your profit may lose some of its purchasing power through inflation. Various investment vehicles (equities and property are examples) are amongst the various ways of addressing inflation risk over the long term.
Interest rate risk	Fluctuations in interest rates not only affect repayment amounts on borrowings if linked to base rate, but can also have a substantial effect on return on outside investments.
Key people risk	Your practice may be reliant on key individuals who have contributed to its success. How would you manage without them if they decide that they are unable to continue with you in the new NHS? If your practice offers private services through key people, their departure could be a blow to your long-term strategy.
Economic risk	This is a measure of how people's expenditure is related to general economic climate. A downturn in the economy may impact on patients' choice of treatment options and particularly in the private sector.
Competitive risk	New practices opening in the area may create competitive risk. In an area where PCTs are challenged with lack of availability of NHS services, growth funding and generous grants may be available to new entrants whose recruitment efforts may target members of your team. In contrast, where there are ample Providers, PCTs may invite tenders for limited growth funds which may drive the tender price down due to the known competition.
Demographic risk	Changes in demographic profiles will affect needs and wants of your patients. Expanding your practice and accepting high need patients where your contract value is based on low need groups will affect your practice's ability to deliver the additional UDA requirements.
Political risk	The likelihood that changes to NHS dentistry will materially affect the way in which dental care is delivered and how the contract is monitored. It may have implications in financial risk areas for any practice wholly or almost wholly dependent on NHS funding.

Table 19: Understanding business risk.

17 CHANGE MANAGEMENT

2006 will be remembered as the year when the GDS mind-set changed. The removal of the restrictions that were associated with the old GDS has sanitised clinical decision-making. The shift from items of treatment to courses of treatment has presented us with a new currency – the Unit of Dental Activity (UDA).

These changes have affected all stakeholders who need to understand the principles of change management if, to paraphrase Bill Clinton, we want the future to be less than an inheritance but more of an opportunity and an obligation.

The process of change

There are three ways to look at the change process.

1 **Planned and emergent change**

Before April 1 2006, the details of the new GDS Contract were known. There was more information – and misinformation, it must be said – about the new contract than was generally believed to be the case. Armed with this knowledge, dentists were able to plan for change. Planned change is the outcome of the conscious assimilation and reasoning of known facts and challenges. It allows people to manage a different working environment better.

But things have changed since 1 April 2006. The Department of Health has issued a number of factsheets to help stakeholders better manage the contract, and information about the outcomes of some of disputes that were forwarded to the NHS Litigation Authority have now been published. New information, data and the strategic thinking of commissioners are constantly changing. Dentists must keep pace with these developments; they need to think on their feet to manage the constant change. This is the challenge of emergent change. We must recognise that we can facilitate the process of change by careful analysis, insightful planning and a well thought-out strategy, remembering that the effects of chance and uncertainty can throw us off course. This is discussed later in this chapter.

2 Episodic and continuous change

Another useful way of looking at change management is to distinguish between episodic change and continuous change. Episodic change has been described as 'infrequent, discontinuous and intentional'. It is sometimes referred to as 'radical or second order change' and usually involves the displacement of one strategy for another. In contrast, continuous change is 'ongoing, evolving and continuous' and is also described as 'incremental or first order change'.

Your long-term vision for your practice will be realised through the process of incremental change, but along the way you will periodically need to implement smaller more radical polices to stay on the road to your vision. Without this vision, few practices will achieve their full potential under the new National Health Service.

3 Developmental, transitional and transformational change

Anderson *et al.* (2001).

Another perspective drawing on these typologies and shown in Table 20 is found in *Beyond Change Management*.

Type of change	Characteristics
Developmental	This may be planned or emergent; it is 'first order', or incremental. It is change that enhances or adjusts existing aspects of your practice, often focusing on the improvement of a particular aspect – refining your systems and processes for recalls, for example in recognition of NICE guidance.
Transitional	The purpose of this is to achieve a known desired state that is different from the existing one. It is episodic, planned and 'second order', or radical. Voluntary Personal Dental Services (PDS) was an example of this – it helped those who were involved to look at so-called 'new ways of working'.
Transformational	This is radical or 'second order' change. It requires a shift in your thinking. Transformation can result in a practice that differs significantly in terms of its culture and strategy. It can help create a practice that operates in developmental mode: one that is continuously learning, adapting and improving – essentially the objective of clinical governance.

Table 20: Types and characteristics of change.

If we now take these aspects of change, we can adapt the theory to the working practice by relating the different facets into a four-quadrant matrix. Professor Gus Pennington is the Chief Executive of the Higher Education Staff Development Agency and he has done just this by plotting the character of a proposed change along a scale to understand how difficult the introduction of any particular initiative might be and how it relates to risk and disturbance (Figure 35).

Pennington (2003).

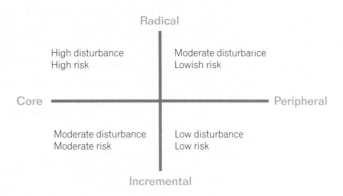

Figure 35: Four-quadrant matrix.

The changes involving the contract will be seen as some as falling into the high risk and high disturbance category but as low disturbance and low risk by many others. When this issue was discussed at the *newcontracthelp* seminars, this book's authors concluded that the difference in perception amongst the dentists related directly to their degree of knowledge, understanding and awareness of the key issues of the changes. In other words, those who were better prepared for the changes and understood the issues were able to manage the process of change more effectively with less disruption and risk.

Change in the NHS

Department of Health, 1998.

In the White Paper *A First Class Service*, The National Co-ordinating Centre of the NHS Service and Organisation Programme (NCCSDO) was commissioned to undertake a review of the evidence in the fields of change management. It has since published two texts under the title *Managing Change in the NHS*, with a target audience which includes 'managers, professionals and researchers involved in change management issues across the NHS'. It is highly unlikely that these publications are known to dentists because dentistry has never been truly integrated with the NHS – until now – and many NHS publications never appear on the general dental practice radar.

The NCCSDO made reference to the concept of 'emergent change' in the first chapter of its first publication, suggesting that:

> Managers make a number of decisions apparently unrelated to the change that emerges. These decisions may be based on unspoken, and sometimes unconscious, assumptions about the organisation, its environment and the future and are, therefore, not as unrelated as they first seem. Such implicit assumptions dictate the direction of the seemingly disparate and unrelated decisions, thereby shaping the change process by 'drift' rather than by design.

> External factors (such as the economy, competitors' behaviour, and political climate) or internal features (such as the relative power of different interest groups, distribution of knowledge, and uncertainty) influence the change in directions outside the control of managers. Even the most carefully planned and executed change programme will have some emergent impacts.

These are crucial observations in the climate of the 2006 contract, where dentists have been reporting apparently unplanned actions and initiatives undertaken by the PCT and the PCTs in turn have been expressing their concerns about insufficient guidance from the Department of Health. The overall picture may be one of confusion, chaos and uncertainty but in reality is a portrait of emergent strategy.

Organisational change in the NHS is complex, as it involves:

- changing pressures in the environment
- multiple stakeholders within and outside the organisation
- changing technologies available to those stakeholders
- complex organisations in which individuals and teams are interdependent – that is, they can only achieve their objectives by relying on other people seeking to achieve different objectives
- people who have experience of change interventions which have had unforeseen or unintended consequences.

If the NHS is to fulfil the ambitions of the *NHS Plan*, then it needs to embrace emergent change; as stakeholders we must understand what this means.

> The complexity and size of the NHS means that managers and professionals are always working on several levels at once. They are dealing with a range of pressures from the centre, for example, and also with immediate local demands. In other words, they are working with multiple priorities competing for time.

These are the words of the authors of the NCCDSO publication and they paint a picture of complexity and organisational pressures that may not be immediately obvious to practising clinicians. We need to be aware of these and tolerant of what can at times seem chaos and disorganisation at local level.

With the increasing involvement of dentists in PCTs as a direct result of the 2006 contract, both sides are becoming more aware of the key issues that impact on organisational performance. This collaborative approach is to be encouraged, as it fosters more effective long-term working relationships. Liaison groups comprising Local Dental Committee and PCT representatives now exist in many areas and provide opportunities for information, exchange and discussion. The dentists who sit on the groups are, to adopt the terms used in *The Fifth Discipline*, 'players'. The author of *The Fifth Discipline*, Peter M Senge, states that there are a number of

Senge (1994).
'positions' players can adopt along a continuum of change and that their response can be gauged and their response reflects their disposition.

There will be many perspectives on how certain clauses of the contract will be interpreted by PCTs and the degree of flexibility that will be permissible. Many of the ambiguous clauses will be a matter of local interpretation, relying on the outcome of the deliberations between PCT managers and local representatives.

Disposition	Player's response to the change
Commitment	Want change to happen and will work to make it happen. Are willing to create whatever structures, systems and frameworks are necessary for it to work.
Enrolment	Want change to happen and will devote time and energy to making it happen within given frameworks. Act within the spirit of the frameworks.
Genuine compliance	See the virtue in what is proposed, do what is asked of them and think proactively about what is needed. Act within the letter of the frameworks.
Formal compliance	Can describe the benefits of what is proposed and are not hostile to them. Do what they are asked but no more. Stick to the letter of the frameworks.
Grudging compliance	Do not accept that there are benefits to what is proposed and do not go along with it. Do enough of what is asked of them not to jeopardise position. They voice opposition and hope for failure. Interpret the letter, not necessarily the spirit, of the frameworks.
Non-compliance	Do not accept that there are benefits and have nothing to lose by opposing the proposition. Will not do what is asked of them. Work outside frameworks.
Apathy	Neither support nor oppose the proposal, just serve time. Do not care about the frameworks.

Table 21: Commitment and compliance in change.

The choice of professional representatives is critical because there will be a range of 'dispositions' on a range of issues; from a negotiating point of view, dentists will need to commit to some, offer formal compliance to others and enrol on the rest. If representatives adopt an adversarial mindset and automatically adopt a position of non-compliance and apathy on all local issues, that is a recipe for a frustrated relationship which will not bode well for the future.

Marshall *et al*, writing in the *British Medical Journal* in 2003 about managing change in the culture of general medical practice, noted that:

> The political imperative to deliver rapid objective change can lead managers to adopt an increasingly authoritarian style. Such an approach may be effective in producing short-term measurable change, but it is likely to bring managers into direct conflict with doctors who value their professional autonomy and resist current attempts to 'manage' their performance.

Marshall *et al.* (2003).

Change Models

Dentists differ in their approach – some have taken a proactive stance and embraced the changes and made substantial changes; others have taken a more reactive stance, preferring to wait for things to 'settle down' and then deciding on what needs to be done and how it should be done.

This is to be expected, even predicted. In 1995, the fourth edition of Everett Rogers' book called *Diffusion of Innovations* was published. In it, he describes his 'adoption curve' which is based on his earlier work in the 1960s. Rogers' view is that the individuals in any system do not adopt an innovation at the same time. Rather, they adopt it over time sequence. To reflect this observation, he classified individuals into adopter categories on the basis of when they first begin using new ideas. He suggested that:

- *Innovators* account for 2.5 per cent of individuals in a system.
- *Early Adopters* account for 13.5 per cent.
- The *Early Majority* account for 34 per cent.
- The *Late Majority* also accounts for 34 per cent.
- *Laggards* make up the remaining 16 per cent.

Where would you place your practice in this continuum of change?

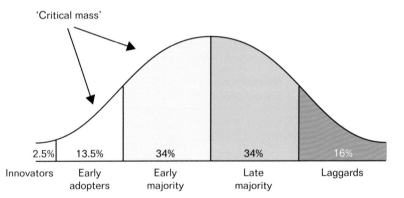

Figure 36: The continuum of change.

According to Rogers, innovators are the pioneers. The early adopters tend to be opinion-leaders to whom potential adopters will look to for advice and guidance – the most influential group as far as diffusion of the message is concerned. Ideas are passed amongst professionals during professional and social interactions before others start to join in. (This was certainly true for those who entered voluntary PDS Arrangements.) The early and later majorities collectively are the mainstream, with the early majority adopting the idea just before 50 per cent of the profession. The late majority are more sceptical, with the laggards using the past as the reference point and are suspicious of change. The early and late majorities make up the core 68 per cent of the curve as defined by the first standard deviation.

The early experience of the new contract bears out Rogers' observation that:

> The early adopter is respected by his or her peers, and is the embodiment of successful, discrete use of new ideas. The early adopter knows that to continue to earn this esteem of colleagues and to maintain a central position in the communication networks of the system, he or she must make judicious innovation-decisions. The early adopter decreases uncertainty about a new idea by adopting it, and then conveying a subjective evaluation of the innovation to near-peers through interpersonal networks.

The change champion

PCTs need change champions if new initiatives and new thinking are to grow in a given area. The change champion will make an excellent change agent, though they may not always want the excess work associated with the change. These are the early adopters: dentists who want the change implementation to succeed, and believe that the change will be beneficial.

The change champions are the natural marketeers for the organisational change and act as catalysts for others. They will speak positively about the change, show that it can be done and support colleagues at an informal level. They give recognition when new behaviours are demonstrated.

Chaos and complexity

One of the barriers to effective implementation of new ways of working is the uncertainty and perceived complexity of the changes. One disturbing observation amongst dentists about the pre-implementation phase of the 2006 contract were the reported variations amongst PCTs when it came to discussions about contract values and UDA targets. The data from the then Dental Practice Board had to be recalculated in some cases when anomalies had been identified. In the case of practices that had part of their test period under PDS arrangements, UDA targets were open to negotiation and the calculation methodology was not consistent amongst PCTs, given that there were significant variations in activity levels for many practices for the GDS and PDS phase of their test period. All this added complexity and confusion to the entire process.

Stacey (1996).

Professor Ralph Stacey has studied how the degree of complexity and consensus impacts on the marketplace. He maps these two variables in his 'Agreement and Certainty matrix' and attributed characteristics to the outcome (Figure 37). As he says:

> This is a method to select the appropriate management actions in a complex adaptive system based on the *degree of certainty* and *level of agreement* on the issue in question.

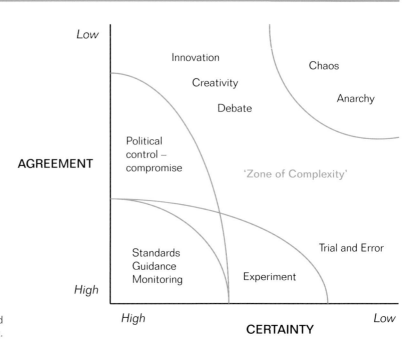

Figure 37: Stacey's Agreement and Certainty matrix.

The introduction of the new contract positioned many general dental practitioners in a zone where there was low agreement/consensus about the changes and great uncertainty – it was no surprise that many meetings around the contract were characterised by vigorous debate fuelled by passionate rhetoric.

Traditional decision-making takes place in the lower left segment of the Agreement and Certainty matrix and dentists have not been in the complexity zone before – it is an area we have so far avoided. To work in this zone requires different skills and alternative processes and change in this zone must be supported. By increasing our knowledge and understanding of the new NHS and working with the local PCT in a collaborative way, we can shift our position from this zone back towards the lower left corner of the matrix.

The 7S model

Waterman (1980).

The 7S approach was developed by business consultants Waterman, Peters and Phillips in 1980 for the US management consultancy McKinsey. They suggested that there were seven aspects of an organisation that needed to harmonise with one another before an organisation could be considered to be 'organised'. The model is a very useful framework for general dental practice. The elements are:

- **Strategy:** This is your plan or course of action to reach your identified goals.
- **Structure:** The salient features of your practice and how they connect.

- **Systems:** The procedures and routine processes that drive the day-to-day running of your practice. Examples include appointment control, the recall system and the fee collection process.
- **Staff:** Personnel categories within the practice – dentists, dental care professionals, specialists, etc.
- **Style:** Characterisation of the behavioural elements with in your practice.
- **Shared values:** The guiding concepts that your practice imbues in its team.
- **Skills:** Distinctive capabilities of key personnel and the practice as a whole.

The inter-relationships are shown in Figure 38.

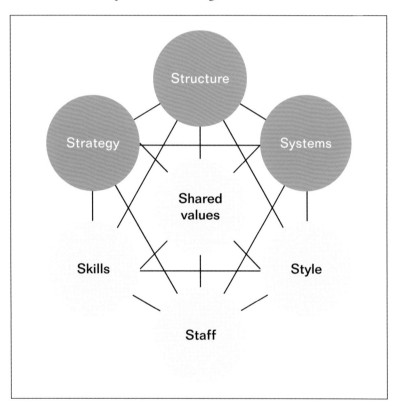

Figure 38: The 7S model.

This model can be used to:

- Identify the strength and weaknesses in your practice. For example, is there a Performer who is not singing from the same song sheet when it comes to working practices in the 2006 contract?
- Show the linkages between the S's and the impact change will have on all the others.

◗ p 231. You can use the template shown in the **Annex** to this chapter to help you with this process. If a planned change is to be effective, then changes in one S must be accompanied by complementary changes in the others.

Tipping point leadership

Malcolm Gladwell was named one of *Time Magazine*'s 100 most influential people in 2005 and is the author of *The Tipping Point: How Little Things Make a Big Difference* (2000). The book has inspired business thinking all over the world and is the inspiration behind W Chan Kim and Renée Mauborgne's model 'Tipping Point Leadership' which explains the four hurdles that block change and how the 'tipping point' strategy can knock them over quickly.

Kim *et al.*, Tipping (2003);
Kim *et al.*, Tipped (2003), p 28.

Kim and Mauborgne's research identified four hurdles that get in the way of optimum performance:

- the team does not understand why change is necessary
- there are limited resources
- employees are demoralised
- there is political opposition to change, both internal and external.

The tipping point strategy outlines how to jump these hurdles.

● **Wake up your practice to the need for radical change**
To inspire fast change that is internally driven by people's own motivation, they need to experience reality first-hand. Internal auditing should result in a face to face analysis of problems/poor performance. The operational realities should be plain. Interestingly, Providers who have been the subject of the Dental Reference Service (DRS) scrutiny in the early days of the 2006 contract have often remarked on the value of the record card checks and audits and the practice inspections where these have been requested by the PCTs. It has allowed Providers to put Performers into the front line and helped to underline the importance of critical issues like noting recall intervals in relation to NICE guidance. Prior to the DRS scrutiny, one Provider had commented that his Performers were not taking the clinical guidelines seriously and ignoring the requirement to follow it in Clause 71 of the standard GDS contract.

● **Focus on the hot spots**
Hot spots are the activities with low-resource input but high-potential performance gains. You can focus on these by allocating the resources appropriately, to the hot spots (the actions that have the greatest impact but are resource-starved) and away from the cold spots (the activities that consume the greatest resources but have little impact on performance).

● **Motivate your key influencers**
Avoid a top-down hierarchical approach. Everyone in the practice should work in unison and move into new areas as one. Concentrating your efforts on your key influencers amongst your team will take less time and effort. If they are well respected, they will be persuasive. With them on board, the rest will follow quickly.

● **Knock down the political hurdles**
Rather than fighting alone, Kim and Mauborgne advise getting a higher and wider voice to fight with you – both internally and externally. The external role can be taken up by the LDC/PCT liaison groups come into play, provided they are aligned to your vision and mindset.
Within your practice, those who are will thus aligned be your 'angels', while those who are have something to lose are likely to oppose your efforts. You should get support from your angels first: this should help to isolate the detractors.

Summary

The 2006 contract has changed the structure and management of general dental practice. It involves a radical rethink about how practices should be managed and also about the most effective ways to deliver patient care. With fixed budgets and UDA targets to meet there are financial challenges with regards to cost control for variable expenses like laboratory bills and consumables. The NICE recall guidance, the abolition of the treatment restrictions that were in the Statement of Dental Remuneration, and the concept of Courses of Treatments all present a range of clinical challenges. The refining of the methods of paying Performers and managing capacity at the practice presents a host of business challenges. The devolution of funds and management responsibility to local level has presented the challenges of relationship management. In fact, almost everything has changed except the primary duty of care to the patient.

In the context of this background of change, practices need to be re-engineered if they are to prepare for the future. Re-engineering is the fundamental rethinking and radical redesign of business processes which can achieve dramatic improvements in measures of performance such as service, quality cost and speed. The direction for the radical rethink must come unequivocally from the top; it remains a leadership issue for the Provider. In his book *Smart Business*, Jim Botkin states that many people in business

Botkin (1999).

fail to see the forest for the trees. This is not an either/or problem. The trick is to see both the forest and the trees.

We need to adopt this philosophy when preparing for the future in the NHS.

There will be many challenges in the future for all practices including those that are predominantly NHS, those that are 'mixed practices', and those that are largely private. Whilst the strategies may differ amongst them, they share the objective of providing quality care in an ethical and profitable way. They also share the same variables in the success equation – an equation in which the only constant is change. How well you manage that constant today will shape your practice tomorrow.

ANNEX
The 7S template

	Style	Shared values	Skills	Staff	Systems	Structure	Strategy
Strategy							■
Structure						■	
Systems					■		
Staff				■			
Skills			■				
Shared values		■					
Style	■						

Works cited

- Akram *et al.* (2010) – Akram S, D'Cruz L. Implementing NICE guidance on recall intervals into General Practice. *Dental Update* 2010; **37**

- Anderson *et al.* (2001) – Anderson D, Ackerman Anderson L. *Beyond Change Management.* Indianapolis: Jossey Bass Wiley, 2001

- Bain (2003) – Bain C. *Treatment Planning in general dental practice – a problem based approach.* Churchill Livingstone, 2003

- Barber (2010) – Barber M W. General dental practitioner views on providing alcohol related health advice – an exploratory study. *British Dental Journal* 2010; **208**: 304–5

- Bedi *et al.* (2005) – Bedi R, Gulati N, McGrath C. A study of satisfaction with dental services among adults in the United Kingdom. *British Dental Journal* 2005; **198**: 433–7

- Beirne *et al.* (2005) – Beirne P, Forgie A, Worthington H V, Clarkson J E. Routine scale and polish for periodontal health in adults. *The Cochrane Database of Systematic Reviews* 2005; Issue 1

- Beirne *et al.* (2007) – Beirne P, Clarkson J E, Worthington H V. Recall intervals for oral health in primary care patients. *The Cochrane Database of Systematic Reviews* 2007; Issue 4

- Berry (2007) – Berry D *New NHS complaints system – consultation.* BDA Policy and Knowledge Directorate, August 2007

- Botkin (1999) – Botkin J. *Smart Business: How Knowledge Communities Can Revolutionize Your Company.* New York: Free Press, 1999

- Cameron *et al.* (1991) – Cameron K, Freeman S. Culture, congruence, strength and type: relationships to effectiveness. *Research in Organizational Change and Development* 1991; **5**: 23–58

- Chestnutt *et al.* (2009) – Chestnutt G, Davies L, Thomas D R. Practitioners perspectives and experiences of the new national Health Service dental contract. *British Dental Journal* 2009; **206**: E18

- Coates (2009) – Coates J. Trouble free tendering. *BDA News* June 2009; **22**: No 1

- D'Cruz (2008) – D'Cruz L The successful management of complaints – turning threats into opportunities. *Dental Update* 2008; **35**: 182–6.

- D'Cruz (2009) – D'Cruz L. Who cares for the carers? *British Dental Journal* 2009; **207**: 11–12

- Davies *et al.* (1998) – Davies H T O, Lampel J. Trust in performance indicators? *Quality in Health Care* 1998; 7: 159–62

- Dyer *et al.* (2006) – Dyer T A, Robinson P G. General health promotion in general dental practice – the involvement of the dental team. Part 2: a qualitative and quantitative investigation of the views of practice principals in South Yorkshire. *British Dental Journal* 2006; **201**: 45–51

- Donabedian (2003) – Donabedian A. *An introduction to Quality Assurance in Healthcare.* New York: Oxford University Press, 2003

- FGDP (2003) – Faculty of General Dental Practice. *Pathways in Practice Volume 1* 3rd Edition (2003)

- Fox (2010) – Fox, C. What do dentists mean by 'prevention' when applied to what they do in their practices? *British Dental Journal* 2010; **208**: 359–63

- Holmes *et al.* (2008) – Holmes R D, Donaldson C, Exley C, Steele J G. Managing resources in NHS dentistry: the views of decision makers in primary care organisations. *British Dental Journal* 2008; **205**: E12

- Hughes (1990) – Hughes D. The reorganisation of the National Health Service: The rhetoric and reality of the internal market. *Modern Law Review* 1990; **54**: 88–103; reprinted in Kennedy and Grub, *Medical Law*. Third Edition. London: Butterworths, 2000.
- Jones *et al.* (2009) – Jones C L, Rooney E. The procurement of NHS dental services – a guide. *British Dental Journal* 2009; **206**: 535–9
- Kaplan *et al.* (1992) – Kaplan, R S and Norton, D P. *The Balanced Score card.* Boston: Harvard Business School Press, 1992
- Kidd *et al.* (2003) – Kidd E A M, Smith B G N, Watson T F. *Pickards Manual of Operative Dentistry.* Oxford University Press 8th Edition (2003)
- Kim *et al.*, Tipping (2003) – Kim W Chan, Mauborgne R. Tipping Point Leadership. *Harvard Business Review*, April 2003
- Kim *et al.*, Tipped (2003) – Kim W Chan, Mauborgne R. Tipped for the Top. *People Management*, 24 July 2003
- McCallum (2007) – McCallum S .The risk management role of the NHSBSA in NHS primary care dentistry; beyond payments and processing. *Dental Profile Magazine* February 2007; No 53: 17–21.
- Marshall *et al.* (2003) – Marshall M, Mannion R, Nelson E, Davies H. Managing change in the culture of general practice: qualitative case studies in primary care trusts. *British Medical Journal* September 2003; **327**
- Mettes (2005) – Mettes D. Insufficient evidence to support or refute the need for 6-monthly dental check-ups. *Evidence-Based Dentistry* 2005; **6(3)**: 62–3
- Mjor (1993) – Mjor I A. Repair versus replacement of failed restorations *International Dental Journal* 1993; **43**: 466–72
- Mjor *et al.* (2002) – Mjor I A, Gordan V V. Failure, repair, refurbishing and longevity of restorations. *Operative Dentistry* 2002 Sep–Oct; **27(5)**: 528–34
- Mount *et al.* (2005) – Mount G J, Hume W R. *Preservation and Restoration of tooth structure.* 2nd edition. Brisbane: Knowledge Books and Software, 2005
- Murray (1996) – Murray J J. Attendance patterns and oral health. *British Dental Journal* 1996; **181**: 339–342
- Muthukrishnan *et al.* (2007) – Muthukrishnan A, Owens J, Bryant S, Dummer P M H. Evaluation of a system for grading the complexity of root canal treatment. *British Dental Journal* 2007 **202** E26
- Pennington (2003) – Pennington G. *Guidelines for Promoting and Facilitating Change.* LTSN Generic Centre, 2003
- Raja *et al.* (2006) – Raja A, Aukett J. Smoking cessation and the dental team. *Dental Update* April 2006: 33175–184
- Rattan *et al.* (2002) – Rattan R, Chambers R, Wakely G. *Clinical Governance in General Dental Practice.* Oxford: Radcliffe Medical Press, 2002
- Rattan (2007) – Rattan, R. *Quality Matters: From Clinical Care to Customer Service.* Quintessence Publishing Co Ltd, 2007
- Rattan *et al.* (2004) – Rattan R, Tiernan J. *Risk Management in General Dental Practice.* New Malden: Quintessence Publishing, 2004
- Rattan (2008) – Rattan R. Weights and measures. *The Dentist* February 2008, pp 26–28

Works cited, references and further reading

- Richmond *et al.* (1992) – Richmond S, O'Brien K D, Buchanan I and Burden D. *An Introduction to Occlusal Indices.* Manchester: Mandent Press, 1992
- Richmond *et al.* (1992) – Richmond S, Shaw W C, Anderson M, Roberts C T. Methods to determine outcome of orthodontic treatment in terms of improvement and standards. *European Journal of Orthodontics* 1992; **14**: 125–39
- RCS (2001) – Royal College of Surgeons. *Restorative Dentistry Index of Treatment Need Complexity Assessment.* Department of Health and Clinical Effectiveness Committee, 2001
- Scally *et al.* (1998) – Scally G, Donaldson L J. Clinical governance and the drive for quality improvement in the new NHS in England. *BMJ* 1998; **317**: 61–5
- Schanschieff *et al.* (1986) – Schanschieff S, Shovelton D, Toulmin J. *Report of the committee of enquiry into unnecessary dental treatment.* London: HMSO 1986
- Senge (1994) – Senge P. *The Fifth Discipline.* New York, Currency, 1994
- Sharif *et al.* (2010) – Sharif, Fedorowicz, Tickle and Brunton, Repair or replacement of restorations: do w e accept built in obsolescence or do we improve the evidence? *British Dental Journal* 2010; **209** 171–4
- Singh *et al.* (2007) – Singh R. Department of Health Prevention Roadshow. Manchester 2007.
- Stacey (1996) – Stacey R. *Complexity and Creativity in Organizations.* San Francisco: Berrett-Koehler, 1996
- Waterman *et al.* (1980) – Waterman R H, Peters T J, Phillips J R. Structure is not organisation. *Business Horizons*, June 1980
- Weerakone *et al.* (2003) – Weerakone S and Dhopatkar A. Clinical Outcome Monitoring Program (COMP): a new application for use in orthodontic audits and research. *American Journal of Orthodontics and Dentofacial Orthopaedics* 2003; 123: 503–11

References

NHS Dental Contract, 2006

- Choosing better oral health: An oral health plan for England Department of Health November 2005 available at www.dh.gov.uk/dental
- Commissioning Specialist Dental Services GRerence 5865 – revised 8 December 2005 available at www.dh.gov.uk/dental
- Factsheets: Implementing Local Commissioning for Primary Care Dentistry available at www.primarycarecontracting.nhs.uk or www.dh.gov.uk/dental
- The General Dental Services and Personal Dental Services Transitional Provisions Order 2005 (SI 2005/3435) (the Transitional Order) www.opsi.gov.uk/si/si2005/20053435.htm
- The General Dental Services: Statement of Financial Entitlements available at www.dh.gov.uk/dental
- The Health and Social Care (Community Health and Standards) Act 2003: www.opsi.gov.uk/ACTS/acts2003/20030043.htm
- The National Health Service (Dental Charges) Regulations 2005 www.opsi.gov.uk/si/si2005/20053477.htm
- The National Health Service (General Dental Services Contracts) Regulations 2005 (SI 2005/3361) (the GDS Regulations) www.opsi.gov.uk/si/si2005/20053361.htm
- The National Health Service (Personal Dental Services Agreements) Regulations 2005 (SI 2005/3373) (the PDS Regulations) www.opsi.gov.uk/si/si2005/20053373.htm
- The National Health Service (Performers Lists) Amendment Regulations 2005 (SI 2005/3491) (the Performers Lists Regulations) www.opsi.gov.uk/si/si2005/20053491.htm
- The National Health Service (Performers Lists) Regulations 2004 (SI2004/585) www.opsi.gov.uk/si/si2004/20040585.htm
- The Personal Dental Services: Statement of Financial Entitlements available at www.dh.gov.uk/dental
- The Standard General Dental Services Contract available at www.dh.gov.uk/dental
- The Standard Personal Dental Services Agreement available at www.primarycarecontracting.nhs.uk or www.dh.gov.uk/dental

To keep updated on the New Contract

Chief Dental Officer, Department of Health: www.dh.gov.uk/AboutUs/HeadsOfProfession/ChiefDentalOfficer/fs/en

NHS Business Services Authority (BSA) formerly Dental Practice Board: www.dpb.nhs.uk

New Contract Help website: www.newcontracthelp.co.uk

Primary Care Contracting website: www.primarycarecontracting.nhs.uk

Dental Organisations

British Dental Association website: www.bda.org

Confederation of Dental Employers website: www.codeuk.com

Dental Defence Union (DDU): www.the-ddu.com

Dental Practitioners Association www.uk-dentistry.org/

Works cited, references and further reading

Dental Protection (DPS): www.dentalprotection.org
Faculty of General Dental Practice website: www.fgdp.org.uk
General Dental Council: www.gdc-uk.org
The Medical and Dental Defence Union of Scotland (MDDUS): www.mddus.com

Clinical Governance

BDA Good Practice Scheme: www.bda.org
CODE Clinical Governance Made Simple (CGMS): www.codeuk.com/clinical-governance.php
Smile-on Clinical Governance package: www.smile-on.com/cg/cgscheme.php

Further reading

- *The 2003 Children's Dental Health Survey.* Office of National Statistics www.statistics.gov.uk/children/dentalhealth/
- *Adult Dental Health Survey: Oral Health in the United Kingdom.* The Stationery Office
- *Audit Commission Report: Dentistry, primary dental care services in England and Wales.* Audit Commission, 2002
- *Dental Recall interval between routine dental examinations:* National Institute for Clinical Excellence, October 2004
- *Equity and excellence: Liberating the NHS,* Department of Health, July 2010
- *Framework proposals for primary dental services in England from 2005.* Department of Health, 6 February 2004 (GR 2755)
- *Implementing a Scheme for Dentists with Special Interests (DwSIs).* Department of Health / Faculty of General Dental Practitioners (UK), May 2004 (GR 2788)
- *NHS Dentistry: Options for Change.* Department of Health, August 2002
- *The NHS Oral Health assessment April 2006.* Department of Health (GR 6503)
- *The NHS Plan: a plan for investment, a plan for reform.* Department of Health, July 2000 (Cm 4818-I)
- *Report of Sir Kenneth Bloomfield: Fundamental Review of Dental Remuneration.* Department of Health, December 2002
- *Select Committee on Health Report.* Access to NHS Dentistry, March 2001
- Kaplan R S, Norton D P. Putting the Balanced Score card to Work. *Harvard Business Review* 71 No 5 (September–October 1993)
- Kay E. *A Modern Concept of Oral Health.* Booklet 1. Denplan Dental Update Series, 2005
- Robinson R, Patel D, Pennycate R. *The Economics of Dental Care.* Office of Health Economics, June 2004

ABBREVIATIONS

ACVPs: Annual Contact Value Payments

ADSSP: Annual Domiciliary and Sedation Services Payments

BDA: British Dental Association

BNUDA: Baseline Number of Units of Dental Activity

BSA: Business Services Authority

CDO: Chief Dental Officer

CoT: Course of treatment

CPD: Continuing Professional Development

CQC: Care Quality Commission

DH: Department of Health

DRO: Dental Reference Officer

DRS: Dental Reference Service

DSD: Dental Services Department

DwSIs: Dentists with Special Interest

GDC: General Dental Council

GDS: General Dental Services

GR: Gateway Reference (publications)

HMRC: HM Revenue and Customs (*formerly Inland Revenue*)

ICAS: Independent Complaints Advocacy Services

IOTN: Index of Orthodontic Treatment Need

NACV: Negotiated Annual Contract Value

NHS: National Health Service

NHSLA: NHS Litigation Authority

NICE: National Institute of Health and Clinical Excellence

PALS: Patient Advice and Liaison Services

PCC: Primary Care Contracting

PCR: Patient Charge Revenue

PCT: Primary Care Trust (*throughout this book the term* Primary Care Trust *will apply equally to the Welsh equivalent,* Local Health Board)

PDS: Personal Dental Services

PHSO: Parliamentary and Health Service Ombudsman

Ⓡ : Marginal abbreviation for GDS Regulations. The internal structure of the Regulations is represented by symbols: **S** for section, **P** for part, **¶** for paragraph, **C** for clause. Hence 'GDS Regulations, Schedule 3 Part 2 6(4)' is represented as Ⓡ S3 P2 6(4).

SDR: Statement of Dental Remuneration

SFE: Statement of Financial Entitlement

UDA: Unit of Dental Activity

UOA: Unit of Orthodontic Activity

VDP: Vocational Dental Practitioner

INDEX